T3-BPX-031

Population and Environmental Biology

Dickenson Series on Contemporary Thought in Biologicial Science

Elof Axel Carlson/Consulting Editor

Bruce H. Carpenter	Molecular and Cell Biology
Edward Glassman	Molecular Approaches to Psychobiology
Elof A. Carlson	Gene Theory
J. Richard Whittaker	Cellular Differentation
Arthur S. Boughey	Population and Environmental Biology
J. Eugene Fox	Molecular Control of Plant Growth
Rodolfo Ruibal	The Adaptations of Organisms

Arthur S. Boughey
University of California,
Irvine

Population and Environmental Biology

Dickenson Publishing Company, Inc., Belmont, California

L. C. Cat. Card No.: 67–21372
Printed in the United States of America

Contemporary Thought in Biological Science

Advances in the biological sciences occur with such a rapidity that the traditional textbook is often out of date before it reaches the student. Furthermore, new contributions to biology are distributed among hundreds of technical journals. Neither the teacher nor the student can cope with this immense and scattered mass of knowledge.

The paperback volumes in this series on Contemporary Thought in Biological Science serve several purposes. Each volume presents a selection of key or illustrative papers in a current field of biology. The editors hope that their selections will stimulate the teacher and the student to increase their awareness of the new advances in biology. Through the teacher's guidance the student may appreciate some of the experimental design and ideas which the research worker presents in his technical publications. Although some of the readings may be difficult and uneven, each article was chosen carefully because of its outstanding illustration of new ideas.

The exposure, in undergraduate courses in biology, to the original articles from which lectures are prepared will also give the student an insight into the creative imagination that the teacher must use to convey these scientific advances to his classes. This series also offers an experimental and flexible approach to teaching biology. New fields may be interdepartmental, and the diversity of concepts which constitute a new segment of knowledge may seem unrelated at first, but in reading these selections the student soon recognizes that these separate contributions lead to a pattern recognizable as a whole. It is this diversity of knowledge and opinion, communicating the excitement of contemporary biological thought, that each volume attempts to convey.

Elof Axel Carlson

Preface

The collection of readings in this book encompasses the fields of taxonomy, systematics, genecology and evolution, and ecology. These fields may be defined as follows: *taxonomy*—the science of the causal interrelationships in living and fossil organisms; *systematics*—the study of the classification of these populations; *genecology* (or *biosystematics*) and *evolution*—the determination of the genetic composition of populations and the processes of change within this; *ecology*—the study of the interaction between populations and their environment.

The classical discipline of systematics, with its modern offshoot, taxonomy, is fast becoming integrated with the science of ecology. Genecological studies of microevolution are becoming as indispensable to the proper understanding of these subjects as, likewise, a knowledge of them is fundamental to the solution of evolutionary problems. All such fields of study are indeed becoming ever more closely associated within the discipline, which can presently only be indicated by the somewhat cumbersome title of *population and environmental biology*—sometimes conveniently, but perhaps misleadingly, shortened to *population biology*. Although no single acceptable term has yet been coined, the better to describe this new discipline, it is very apparent that all aspects of populations—their classification, their genecological behavior, their niche distribution and occurrence, their productivity, and their incorporation into the individual food chains of particular ecosystems—do fall within one and the same single discipline.

No longer can plants and animals be entirely classified solely on the basis of characters subjectively selected from their differing morphology. The genetical cause of their variation must be determined, as well as the significance of particular cytological, physiological, and behavioral factors in microspeciation. The ecological investigation of a plant or an animal now involves considerably more than a study of its physiology and morphology in relation to its habitat. The part that the organism plays in receiving and transmitting energy within the ecosystems where it occurs must be investigated, along with the nature of its breeding system and of the regulatory mechanisms that limit its numbers.

These contemporary readings have been selected to illustrate scientific work dealing with the various aspects of this unified discipline. The publications from which the extracts are taken span the last decade, but a majority of the works have appeared within the last five years. This limited selection from a now already extensive bibliography indicates more expressively than can any short preface the general direction that population and environmental studies are taking. Variation in the genotype—that is, in the genetic constitution of the individual—provides the material on which natural selection can work to evolve new populations. These new populations proceed to occupy more differentiated ecological niches and follow more refined processes of energy transfer. This systematic variation, which the taxonomist must interpret and classify, has a significance that in its ultimate meaning is purely ecological. The biological unit of greatest significance for evolution is not the organism but the *population*. The genetical, physiological, and behavioral responses of any population have to operate within the ecological limits imposed by particular ecosystems.

To cover, in one short volume, this immense field now embraced by population and environmental biology is patently impossible. The thirteen papers appearing here are intended to indicate only the present scope and direction of work in this area. Further literature references, if they are needed, can be obtained from the bibliographies listed in the original publications which are fully cited in the text. For convenience, the readings have been grouped into four sections: Taxonomy, Systematics, Genecology and Evolution, and Ecology—and a brief commentary introduces each section.

Arthur S. Boughey

Irvine, California

Contents

4/Ecology

Population and Environmental Biology

1 / Taxonomy

During the last few years taxonomic principles have been subjected to a critical re-examination. What now emerges may be called essentially a population approach, especially concerned with an examination of taxonomic relationships at the infraspecific level. There is still the danger that this emphasis on populations might promote the erection of an independent and unrelated alternative taxonomic structure, coexisting with the classical system. Indeed, the general application of the *deme terminology,* described in the paper by the British biosystematist J. S. L. Gilmour, might have precisely this result. Another possible source of such an alternative system is indicated in the short extract from the important book by Sokal and Sneath on numerical taxonomy, embodying Adansonian concepts. To the French botanist Adanson is attributed the first use of all available characters in taxonomy, without any special weighting.

Meanwhile, various techniques have been introduced with the intention of extending and refining classical taxonomy. Chromatography has been extensively employed in the study of plant alkaloids and other plant products, sometimes providing additional information useful in the resolution of particular taxonomic problems. A typical example of this use is described in the account by H. P. Riley and T. R. Bryant[1] of the separation of nine species of the Iridaceae by paper chromatography. They showed that species of the genus *Watsonia* resembled one another more closely than they did species of the genera *Dietes, Babiana,* and *Sparaxis.* They considered that since the patterns of species from different genera differ more than the patterns from different species of the same genus, paper chromatography might be a useful addition to conventional taxonomic methods.

The somewhat similar technique of electrophoresis—not yet employed as generally as chromatography—has been used especially for the separation of proteins in blood and in body fluids. The applications of electrophoresis are referred to in the article by Ernst Mayr in the section entitled *Systematics.* In a paper well illustrating this technique, L. E. Brown and H. I. Fisher[2] described the examination of the blood proteins of five species of Procillariiform birds. They found that the genera were well marked and that congeneric species showed the greatest similarities. Now that it has become possible to identify individual DNA molecules, it also may be possible to characterize species by their particular combination not of characters but of types of DNA molecules.

It is only natural in this computer age that attempts should be made to

[1] H. P. Riley, and T. R. Bryant, "The separation of nine species of the Iridaceae by paper chromatography," *Am. Jour. Bot., 48:* 133–37, 1961.

[2] L. E. Brown, and H. I. Fisher, "Electrophoretic study of blood proteins . . . ," *Auk, 83:* 111–16, 1966.

computerize taxonomy. One development of this process is discussed in the paper by E. J. Beers and W. R. Lockhart. This computerization may perhaps be the ultimate achievement in taxonomy, but as yet it has neither gained general acceptance among taxonomists nor been extensively applied either to classical or to numerically determined taxa. A timely and humorous warning is included in the paper by C. B. Heiser, which refers to these various attempts to revitalize classical taxonomy and illustrates the essential need for all scientists occasionally to stand aside and laugh at themselves.

The Deme Terminology

J. S. L. Gilmour

The initial stimulus to produce such a terminology arose from the conviction that the multitude of categories which, by the 1930's, had been proposed for the units of Experimental Taxonomy (alternatively known as Biosystematy and Genecology) contained the seeds of much potential confusion, both as regards the *purpose* of the categories and the *overlap and inter-relationships* of the actual terms used.

The need for such categories stems, of course, from the great development of genetics and cytology which began about the beginning of the century, triggered off by the re-discovery of Mendel's work in 1900. This development gave biologists, for the first time, some knowledge of how micro-evolutionary change actually takes place, and necessitated the creation of a terminology to describe the units of such change. To take one example, Turesson, in Sweden, discovered, by his transplant experiments, that many of the slightly differing populations within a species were genetically distinct and had almost certainly arisen by selection in response to differing ecological conditions. He proposed the term "ecotype" for populations of this kind, and much subsequent work by Gregor, Turrill, Marsden-Jones, and many others, has confirmed that this type of micro-evolutionary change is a widespread phenomenon. Again, the inter-fertility and inter-sterility of populations, in nature and in the experimental ground, is obviously an important factor in their evolution, and categories (such as Danser's Commiscuum, Comparium, and Convivium) were proposed to describe units based on this factor. Gradually, a multitude of categories accumulated; a duplicated report on them compiled a few years ago by Sylvester-Bradley for the Systematics Association ran to nearly twenty pages:

Reprinted by permission of the author and publisher from the Report of the Scottish Plant Breeding Station, Pentlandfield, Scotland, 1960, pp. 99–105.

One important feature of these categories is that the relationship between them and the categories of "orthodox" taxonomy (genera, species, &c.) has very rarely been clearly defined by the authors who put them forward. Are they intended to be additional to, or substitutes for, the "orthodox" categories? This doubt is accentuated when the word "species" is incorporated into an experimental taxonomic term, as it is, for example, in Turesson's "ecospecies."

It is the contention of those putting forward the deme terminology that this is a key question, and that no satisfactory answer can be found without giving some thought to the nature and purpose of classification in general, whether applied to living or non-living things. This approach has been developed elsewhere (Gilmour, 1956) and in this brief article I will make only the following points:—

(1) Every classification should be judged in relation to the *purpose* for which it is made. No classification should be regarded as an end in itself, but as a *tool* to serve a particular need or needs. To say that one classification is "better" than another, without considering *"better" for what purpose,* is to make a virtually meaningless statement.

(2) It is necessary to make different classifications for different purposes. Thus, one makes a different classification of mountains if one is interested in their heights from that made if one is interested in their geology.

(3) In the case of some objects, it is possible to make *one* classification that serves a large number of purposes, in addition to making many other classifications, each serving a particular purpose. The possibility of doing this depends on there being *one* factor influencing the attributes of the objects that is more powerful than any other, thus enabling one to make a classification whose classes contain objects having many attributes in common. For example, in classifying mass-produced motor-cars, the powerful influence of mass-production enables one to classify the individual cars into a number of separate "models," each comprising cars with practically all their attributes in common. Such classifications (of which mass-produced car "models" form an extreme example) are termed, in the general theory of classification, *natural* classifications, and are useful for a wide range of purposes, as opposed to *artificial* classifications (*e.g.*, all cars delivered to a certain town), which class together individuals with very *few* attributes in common, and which are useful virtually only for the purpose for which they were made. Thus, to know that a car belongs to a particular model enables one to predict its price, its speed, its comfort, and many other attributes, whereas to know only that it was a car delivered to Cambridge, is useful almost exclusively for purposes of Cambridge trade statistics. Intermediate classifications would be those into *types* of vehicle (e.g., lorries,* sports cars, &c.) or those based on *age*

* English slang for *trucks*—editor's note.

(*e.g.*, vintage cars, &c.)—intermediate in the number of common attributes, and in usefulness.

If we try to apply these general principles to the classification of living things at or about the species level, I suggest that we find a situation in which, owing to the powerful influence of heredity, it is possible to make *one* classification that is a natural one in the above sense and is, therefore, useful for a wide range of purposes, namely the classification into the orthodox taxonomic categories of species, subspecies, varieties, &c. Such a classification has not necessarily any micro-evolutionary purpose and, indeed, was made long before the fact of evolution was accepted. In order to continue to be useful for a wide range of purposes, it should remain as stable as possible and should be exempt from constant alteration, for either taxonomic or nomenclatural reasons. It should form, as it were, a broad map of the, mainly morphological, variability of living things, a map that is useful alike to the general and applied biologist, to the ecologist, the anatomist, the horticulturist, and the farmer. In addition, however, for special purposes, other classifications can be made, quite distinct from the "orthodox" natural classification, and one such classification can be a classification specifically constructed to study the mechanism of micro-evolutionary change. A difficulty arises here, that has, I suggest, led to much of the confusion surrounding the terminology of experimental taxonomy. In many organisms, especially among animals, the orthodox categories of species, subspecies, &c., based primarily on the correlation of morphological characters, coincide pretty closely with a grouping according to the factors, such as inter-sterility, of importance in micro-evolutionary change, and this coincidence has obscured the desirability of keeping the two classifications distinct. This situation, however, by no means always occurs, and, especially in plants, one often finds, for example, that inter-sterility barriers cut right across a grouping according to morphological similarity.

It is, I suggest, essential, if confusion is to be avoided, for the two classifications, one for a wide range of purposes, and one for the particular purpose of studying the units of micro-evolutionary change, to be kept distinct, both in aim and in terminology. This is the basic point that led to the formulation of the deme terminology, a terminology designed, at the same time, to underline the separation of broad-purpose and micro-evolutionary classifications, and to provide a uniform and workable terminology for the latter.

The full range of terms suggested is contained in the paper published in *Genetica* in 1954; here I will give only the principle on which it is based and a selection of the terms included. The essence of the terminology is the construction of a series of category-terms by the addition of one or more virtually self-explanatory prefixes to the "neutral" suffix

"-deme." The suffix -deme is defined as "a term, always used in this terminology with a prefix, -denoting any group of individuals of a specified taxon." (The use of the phrase "specified taxon" indicates the way in which the "orthodox" categories can be used as a "framework" into which other classifications, for particular purposes, can be fitted.) An important point to note is that the suffix -deme is *neutral;* that is to say, it carries no implication that the individuals exhibit any relationship other than that they belong to a specified taxon. In particular, it carries no implication that they form a *population,* in either a topographical or an interbreeding sense; these, and other implications, are indicated in the terminology by *prefixes.*

The ten basic terms suggested, with their definitions, are as follows:—

TOPODEME: a deme occurring in a specified geographical area.
ECODEME: a deme occurring in a specified kind of habitat.
PHENODEME: a deme differing from others phenotypically.
GENODEME: a deme differing from others genotypically.
PLASTODEME: a deme differing from others phenotypically but not genotypically.
GAMODEME: a deme composed of individuals which are so situated spatially and temporarily that, within the limits of the breeding system, all can interbreed.
AUTODEME: a deme composed of predominantly autogamous individuals.
ENDODEME: a gamodeme composed of predominantly endogamous (*i.e.,* closely inbreeding) dioecious plants (or bisexual animals).
AGAMODEME: a deme composed of predominantly apomictic plants (or asexual animals).
CLINODEME: one of a series of demes which collectively show a specified variational trend (*i.e.,* which collectively form a cline).

Subsequently, the term "cytodeme" has come into use for a deme showing chromosome differences from other demes.

Reference can be made to the *Genetica* paper for a full explanation of these terms, together with examples, but a word may be said here on the term "gamodeme," which is essentially synonymous with the phrase "breeding population" as employed in micro-evolutionary and genetical literature, and hence represents a very basic concept. The term has been taken up to some extent by biologists, but in some cases (e.g., in Huxley, 1942, and in Carter, 1951) the bare suffix "deme-" has been used in place of it, no doubt partly because it is shorter. This usage, it should be emphasised, cuts across the whole idea underlying the deme terminology, as it is essential to keep the suffix -deme completely "neutral," otherwise the connotation of "breeding population" becomes injected into *all* the compound terms, thus destroying the intended use of many of them. For example, the term "ecodeme" is designed to cover *all* individuals of the taxon occurring in a particular type of habitat, right throughout the range of the taxon, and carries no implication that such individuals form one interbreeding population.

In addition to the basic, "first order," derivatives, "second order" derivatives can be constructed, and about two dozen are suggested in the *Genetica* paper. Examples are:—

GENOECODEME: an ecodeme differing from others genotypically.

HOLOGAMODEME: a deme composed of all of those individuals which, within the limits of the breeding system, are believed to be able to interbreed with a high level of freedom under a specified set of conditions (*cf.* Turesson's "ecospecies").

COENOGAMODEME: all hologamodemes considered to be capable of exchanging genes through their members to some extent, but not with freedom, under a specified set of conditions (*cf.* Turesson's "coenospecies").

SYNGAMODEME: all coenogamodemes connected by the ability of some of their members to form viable but sterile hybrids under a specified set of conditions (*cf.* Danser's "comparium").

"Genoecodeme" corresponds broadly with Turesson's "ecotype," and the last three are designed to cover the most important of the situations commonly encountered in the investigation of the fertility relationships of populations.

One point was not perhaps stressed as much as it should have been in the *Genetica* paper, and that is the question of the naming of individual *examples* of the various categories. Some biologists have asked if it was intended that these should be named according to some definite and uniform system—perhaps with Latin names parallel to those of the taxonomic categories. This was certainly not the intention. In some groups, of course, deme categories will coincide with taxonomic categories; for example, genoecodemes with subspecies, and the genoecodemes will then, in effect, have a Latin name *as a subspecies.* It was the intention, however, that the deme categories, *as such,* should be referred to by a loose, *ad hoc,* method of nomenclature, varying with, and adapted to, the particular type of investigation being carried out. For example, if a series of gamodemes in a particular area is being studied, each gamodeme could be referred to by a number or letter, or by a topographical adjective if that were more appropriate.

The above very brief outline will, I hope, give a broad idea of the aim and scope of the deme terminology. Its adoption, in whole or in part, will depend, of course, on the acceptance of the thesis that a "natural" classification is distinct in aim, and should be distinct in terminology, from a micro-evolutionary classification. This point is a fundamental one, and there are signs that it is receiving consideration from biologists; Cain (1959, p. 316) for example, has recently discussed it in relation to the difference between the taxonomic practice of zoologists and botanists. If the deme terminology can claim to have played a part in stimulating this interest, its proposers will feel that it has served a useful purpose.

References

Cain, A. J. (1959). Taxonomic Concepts. *Ibis,* **101,** 302–318.
Carter, G. S. (1951). "Animal Evolution." Sidgwick & Jackson, Ltd., London.
Gilmour, J. S. L. (1951). The development of taxonomy since 1851. *Nature,* **167,** 400.
Gilmour, J. S. L., and Gregor, J. W. (1939). Demes: a suggested new terminology. *Nature,* **144,** 333.
Gilmour, J. S. L., and Heslop-Harrison, J. (1954). The deme terminology and the units of micro-evolutionary change. *Genetica,* **27,** 147–161.
Huxley, J. S. (1942). "Evolution: the Modern Synthesis." George Allen & Unwin, Ltd., London.

Principles of Numerical Taxonomy

Robert R. Sokal
Peter H. A. Sneath

The Basic Positions

Numerical taxonomy is based on the ideas first put forward by Adanson. They may be called Adansonian and are described concisely by the following axioms.

(1) The ideal taxonomy is that in which the taxa have the greatest content of information and which is based on as many characters as possible.

(2) A priori, every character is of equal weight in creating natural taxa.

(3) Overall similarity (or affinity) between any two entities is a function of the similarity of the many characters in which they are being compared.

(4) Distinct taxa can be constructed because of diverse character correlations in the groups under study.

(5) Taxonomy as conceived by us is therefore a strictly empirical science.

(6) Affinity is estimated independently of phylogenetic considerations.

The Estimation of Resemblance

This is the most important and fundamental step in numerical taxonomy. It commences with the collection of information about characters in the taxonomic group to be studied. This information may already exist and merely require extraction from the literature, or it may have to be discovered entirely or partly de novo. In most cases both of these procedures will need to be applied. For the method to be reliable, many characters are needed. At least sixty seem desirable, and less than forty should never be used. All kinds of characters are equally desirable: morphological, physiological, ethological, and sometimes even distributional ones. We must guard only against introducing bias into our choice of characters and against characters which are not an accurate expression of the properties of the organisms.

We assume characters to be equivalent since we believe that there are no special groups of genes related to single morphological regions but that a random sample of the genotype is best obtained by sampling many and various characters. The general occurrence of pleiotropism, as well as the fact that a given character is usually responsive to more than one locus, confirms us in our position.

From our assertion of the equal taxonomic value of every character it is only a small step to the Adansonian practice of equal weight for every character when using it to evaluate taxonomic relationships. This is a point in direct conflict with traditional taxonomic practice and over which much controversy has raged. We . . . would like to mention here only that, granted the desirability of the separation of the measure of resemblance from a study of phylogeny, equal weighting is an almost self-evident logical consequence. We feel reassured in that at least three independent researchers working along somewhat different lines and from different assumptions have all reached the identical conclusion.

The actual computation of a measure of affinity can be done in a variety of ways. Most methods result in coefficients of similarity ranging between unity and zero, the former for perfect agreement, the latter for none whatever. Except in unusual cases the calculations are likely to be rather tedious, and electronic computation will be needed for any but very minor studies.

The similarity coefficients are then tabulated in matrix form with one coefficient for every pair of taxonomic entities. If a symmetrical (mirror image) matrix is to be tabulated for t entities, a $t \times t$ matrix will result with unity in the principal diagonal. This matrix can be represented geometrically by points in a space. A maximum of t dimensions is needed for a correct representation of the t points (taxonomic entities) in the space. The distances between the points are related to taxonomic distances.

Experimental Methods in Computer Taxonomy

R. J. Beers
W. R. Lockhart

Introduction

It has been proposed (Sneath, 1957a,b) that electronic computers be employed to analyse taxonomic data in accord with the Adansonian principle that classification depends on estimates of the overall similarity between organisms, based on examination of a large number of equally weighted features. The general validity of this approach to bacterial systematics has since been demonstrated in a number of investigations (e.g. Bojalil and Cerbón, 1961; Colwell and Liston, 1961; Gilardi *et al.*, 1960; Hill, 1959; Hill *et al.*, 1961; Sneath and Cowan, 1958; Talbot and Sneath, 1960). Despite some manifest shortcomings in procedure, however, most subsequent workers have adhered rather closely to the details of Sneath's original techniques. We now propose some refinements in methodology which may prove useful in extending and strengthening the application of computers to taxonomic problems. The essential axiom of this "school" of systematics is that all properties of organisms are of equal importance in creating taxa; one may make necessary and convenient modifications in techniques without being guilty either of heretical disregard for the basic principles of Adansonian taxonomy or of lack of respect for the creative impetus provided by Sneath.

Methodology—A Critique

For each of the steps involved in the estimation of overall similarity a number of alternatives may exist which are equally valid logically; the more convenient of these methods are chosen in actual practice (Sneath, 1957b). On the basis of the experience since accumulated by numerous workers, it may be well to re-apply the criterion of convenience to some of these alternatives. The established method for calculating similarities between pairs of organisms makes use of the expression

$$S = \frac{n_s}{n_s + n_d}$$

where n_s is the number of features possessed by both organisms and n_d is the number of features possessed by one organism but not the other. Each

Reprinted by permission of the authors from the *Journal of General Microbiology, 28:* 633–40, 1962.

organism is scored as positive (+) or negative (−) for each feature. The symbol (0), for "no comparison," is used when no data are available. Sneath (1957b) used the symbol NC for this purpose. In comparing two organisms, the computer is directed to score (+ +) as a similarity and (+ −) or (− +) as a difference, ignoring (− −) or any combination containing a zero.

However, difficulties arise in scoring certain properties (such as colony morphology) which cannot be considered simply present or absent. In such instances there may be no logical basis for deciding which is the positive trait. It becomes necessary either to make an arbitrary decision to consider, let us say, the smooth colony as positive (in which case two rough strains would not be scored as similar), or to assign two features to colony morphology:

Features	*1*	*2*
Strain A—smooth colonies	+	−
Strain B—rough colonies	−	+

A pair of strains with the same colony type would score a single similarity, but strains differing in colony morphology would score *two* dissimilarities, introducing an unwarranted bias into the calculated S values. We have had some success with a slightly different convention, in which the two colony types are scored:

Features	*1*	*2*
Strain A—smooth colonies	+	−
Strain B—rough colonies	0	+

Use of the (0) symbol prevents a second dissimilarity being scored. This method is convenient also when there are more than two alternatives, as:

Features	*1*	*2*	*3*	*4*
Strain A—smooth colonies	+	−	−	−
Strain B—rough colonies (type I)	0	+	−	−
Strain C—rough colonies (type II)	0	0	+	−
Strain D—mucoid colonies	0	0	0	+

It will be seen that a pair of strains with like colony type will score a single similarity, and that a strain of any colony type will score a single dissimilarity in comparison with any organism differing from it in colonial morphology. An individual strain is scored by rule of thumb: place a (+) under the column for the appropriate feature, then place (0) in each column to the left and (−) in each column to the right. The order in which the features are arranged may be decided arbitrarily, since it will not affect the outcome. Such use of the "no comparison" (0) category as a part of the scoring system rather than simply to indicate that no data are available was made also by Sneath (1957b) in his "Method C" for scoring quantitative data, although for different reasons. No theoretical justification is offered for the scoring method here proposed; it is quite arbitrary, but justifiable if it is found empirically to yield a logical result.

This technique is also useful for scoring quantitatively the response of organisms to a toxic (physical or chemical) environment. Though the usual procedure has been to score all strains as either sensitive or resistant, then to score only the resistant strains on a quantitative basis, it may be argued that there is no such thing as absolute sensitivity or resistance. Any strain will be inhibited when dosage of a toxic agent is great enough, and any strain will be insensitive to sufficiently small concentrations. Thus a given degree of sensitivity may be considered merely as alternative to all other possible states of sensitivity:

Features	*1*	2	3
Strain A—insensitive	+	—	—
Strain B—moderately sensitive	0	+	—
Strain C—highly sensitive	0	0	+

The investigator is spared the embarrassment of stating whether resistance or sensitivity is the positive character, since the outcome is the same in either case:

Features	*1*	2	3
Strain A—insensitive	0	0	+
Strain B—moderately sensitive	0	+	—
Strain C—highly sensitive	+	—	—

We could by similar reasoning extend this argument to include *all* quantitative tests. All we really know about an indole or catalase "negative" culture is that it does not produce enough indole or catalase to give a positive response in the analytical test we have used. Another test, more or less sensitive than the one used, might have given different results. If quantitative tests are included, failure to produce detectable amounts could well be considered as simply one of the alternatives, rather than being scored as a separate property. Two catalase "positive" strains would not then be scored as similar unless they produced approximately equal quantities of catalase, but perhaps they should not be.

It would not be well to pursue this viewpoint too far, however, especially if one were scoring quantitative data in rather small increments. An alternative would be to score the qualitative test as one feature, then to score quantitative data for positive strains by the method already proposed, marking negative strains (0) for "no comparison" in each of the quantitative features. This is similar to the technique presently in use. It has the disadvantage that more comparisons are made between positive than between negative strains, magnifying essentially minor dissimilarities among the former. It is observed in practice that relationships among strains tend to be obscured when too much information of this sort is included. It would seem better to omit questions which cannot legitimately be asked of all organisms being surveyed (e.g. "how much catalase is produced?" when some strains produce none, "what is the shape of the leaves?" when not all the organisms studied have leaves). Such properties are valuable for precise definition of relationships among closely related organisms, and no individual study need be restricted to features applicable to *all* bacteria (Sneath, 1957b), but it would perhaps be wise to include in any given survey only tests which apply to all the organisms actually included in that particular study.

Consideration of the hazards encountered when more criteria of similarity are applied to some individuals than to others leads us to re-examine the convention that only "positive" results are considered as similarities. That is, a test which is scored as negative for both organisms being compared is ignored altogether on the ground that this fact is without significance. As a consequence, since individuals differ in their proportion of positive responses to a given battery of tests, the denominator in the expression

$$S + \frac{n_s}{n_s + n_d}$$

varies for each pair of organisms, and with it varies the statistical significance of individual S values in any survey of the similarities among a group of organisms. This variation is likely to be serious when diverse strains are being studied, or when the battery of tests is not carefully selected to yield approximately the same proportion of positive responses for each strain (which in practice is difficult to attain without bias). Within a relatively homogeneous group of actinomycetes, Gilardi *et al.*, (1960) found a disturbing correlation between the percentage of positive tests for any strain and its highest S value. When the same data were analysed using a parameter (*M*, "matching coefficient") which permitted comparison of properties negative for both strains (Hill *et al.*, 1961), considerably sharper demarcations were obtained between groups. Our own experiments (Beers *et al.*, 1962) indicate that results are more meaningful when negative similarities are included.

In justification for restricting the scoring of similarities to positive responses, Sneath (1957b) stated that the class of negative properties is almost infinite, and that one does not know where to stop. On the other hand, an almost infinite positive class also could be devised. It is no less sensible to consider two bacteria similar because both lack feathers than to consider them similar because both possess cell walls; we must trust to the good judgement of individual investigators to eschew such extremes. The problems encountered in actual practice are likely to be more mundane, if equally troublesome. We have already pointed out that special scoring is necessary for those cases in which there is no logical basis for deciding what should be considered the positive trait. Even for tests in which a "positive" response appears rather obvious, it is not quite safe on genetic grounds to state that negativity constitutes "absence." Although we must score phenotypes, we presume taxa are created ultimately on a genetic basis. When a bacterium fails to ferment lactose, for example, while the failure may be due to the lack of an appropriate genetic determinant, it may equally well result from a modified genetic site causing production of an incomplete or altered enzyme, or from the very positive presence of a modifier gene which inhibits overt expression of fermentative capacity. Hill *et al.* (1961) cited similar arguments in support of their "matching coefficient." Even if the view be accepted that similarity should be based only on positive responses, a recurring dilemma is encountered as to whether positivity is merely illusory for any given test. Rather than to engage in endless debate about how many angels can dance on the heads of each of these pins, it seems better to admit frankly that no compelling theoretical arguments exist either for or against comparing apparently negative results as similarities. We are then free to proceed on the pragmatic basis that we will use which ever scoring convention yields superior results; the available evidence seems to favour permitting comparisons between negatives. The scoring technique already proposed could be used in this way. For example:

Features	*1*	2
Strain A—produces indole	+	—
Strain B—does not produce indole	0	+

This amounts to saying that for any determinable characteristic of an organism there are at least two alternatives, each of equal value in classification. It would seem at first glance simpler to use only one feature in this example, and merely to instruct the computer to accept pairs of negatives as was done by Hill *et al.* (1961) in defining their *M* value. But the proposed scoring method would not then be applicable in instances where there are three or more alternatives. As it is, a single uniform scoring convention may be used in all cases, rather than resorting to different scoring methods (Sneath, 1957b) for different circumstances. Since the expression for calculation of S remains unchanged, it is possible with this scoring technique to count negative comparisons without altering the computer program.

In fact, however, S (or *M*) values may not be the most appropriate parameter for expressing relationships among strains. It usually is possible to define groups with fair precision by comparing S values, but relationships within and among groups are not accurately described in this way. The relationships among organisms in nature appear to be organized not as a hierarchy but as a three-dimensional array. (Actually it may be a multidimensional array, but the state of our present knowledge hardly justifies attempting the rather sophisticated mathematics required to depict such an arrangement.) In constructing three-dimensional models of the spatial relationships among enterobacteria, Lysenko and Sneath (1959) found the simple parameter $1 - S$ inadequate as a measure of distance between individuals or groups. Needing a distance value that would vary from infinity at $S = 0$ to zero at $S = 1.0$, they chose $1/S - 1$ and suggested that $\log 1/S$ would serve equally well. Rogers and Tanimoto (1960), in using computer methods for classifying plants, employed $-\log_2 S (= \log_2 1/S)$ as their distance parameter, pointing out that this defines a semimetric space in which there may be two individuals (or groups) related to a third in such a way that they are not necessarily ralated at all to each other. All such measures have the effect of progessively accentuating the distances between organisms as similarities decrease. In our experiments, we have defined distance as

$$D = \log_2 1/S = \log_2 \frac{(n_s + n_d)}{n_s}.$$

Logarithms to base 2 yield manageable numbers, and are easily handled by digital computers. Finney, Hazlewood and Smith (1955) have prepared convenient tables of logarithms to base 2. We have found D only slightly superior to S as a means of defining groups at high similarities, but it appears to depict intergroup relationships more clearly. Since D, or some alternative measure of distance, seems to express more meaningfully than similarity ratios the relationships among organisms, it would appear desirable to adopt distance as our primary parameter. Such data should prove increasingly useful for comparative purposes as a catalogue of information gradually is accumulated by various investigators working with divers organisms. Since D can be calculated directly, and should be quite adequate also for sorting organisms into groups, S values need not necessarily even be computed.

As we have proposed changing nearly everything else, it may be wondered why we stated earlier that the principle of equally-weighted features is accepted as axiomatic. Although this viewpoint has been defended adequately already (Sneath, 1957a; Rogers and Tanimoto, 1960), some further amplification may be in order. This notion is not palatable to many microbiologists, because they "know" (from previous experience) that some properties of organisms are indeed more significant than others. But one has only to reflect that the experience on which such judgements are based was itself a somewhat unrefined Adansonian process. All that is really being proposed is that we re-examine, by means of the abundance of data and the greater quantitative accuracy possible from the use of computers, our present concepts about which are the important characteristics. We may discover some whose existence we did not suspect; we shall almost certainly learn that others, presently accepted, are of doubtful validity. In any case, *a priori* assumptions of importance for particular tests are not justifiable. Selection of key characteristics necessarily follows rather than precedes the establishment of taxa. Perhaps much of the present confusion stems from a failure to distinguish the quite different functions of classification and diagnosis. Only after we know what groups actually exist in nature need we be concerned with the properties which are characteristic for a given group, that is, of diagnostic value.

The possibilities for diagnosis in the computer approach have been largely overlooked thus far. Although computer techniques can establish groups, the only means of diagnosing a new isolate as a member of one of these would be to repeat the entire calculation with the new strain included. Otherwise, traditional methods would have to be used; inspection of the data would show the essential characteristics of each group, and a key would be constructed. It would not be at all difficult, however, to let the computer furnish us with a quantitative description of each of the groups. The data for all the strains in any group which had been established could be furnished, and the machine instructed to calculate the proportion of positive responses, within that group, for each feature: $P = n/N$, where n is the number of positive responses for any feature and N is the number of strains in the group. If scoring had been done by the method advocated above, it would be necessary to calculate P for only one of each pair of alternative features (though for each feature in properties with more than two alternatives). The value of P would then be a quantitative description of one property of a group, and a catalogue of P values would constitute a diagnostic description of the group. Very high or low values of P (near one or zero) would indicate key diagnostic characteristics. As with any description of a taxon, such data would be useful only when based on observations of an adequate number of strains. The relationship between P and the number of strains on which it was based would readily yield a statistical estimate of the confidence limits for any alleged property of a group.

One can envisage an ultimate taxonomy in which both objectives of systematics—classification and diagnosis—are satisfied by computer methods. Taxa would be developed and defined by means of D values, and future catalogues might consist of lists of appropriate P values for each taxon. A statement that $P = 0.85$ for indole production would be far more helpful than the current "most strains produce indole." Further, computer programs could be designed to do the actual labour of diagnosis. An isolate would be subjected to a suitable battery of tests, and—knowing the characteristic P values (and their confidence limits) for each property of various taxa—the computer could furnish not only a diagnosis but a statistical estimate of the reliability of its own findings. The minimum number and kinds of tests for reasonably accurate diagnosis would have been computed beforehand. Such calculations, while a trifle complex, are well within the programming capacity of modern electronic computers. The charms of such a system of diagnosis are readily apparent to anyone who has had the frustrating experience of trying to trace an unknown isolate through even the best of presently available keys.

Conclusions

It is not our intent to destroy the edifice constructed by many workers on the foundation supplied by Sneath's initial efforts. Only because the structure of this new taxonomy shows itself to be fundamentally sound is it worthwhile to modify it. Any revolutionary development is likely to be somewhat crude in its early stages; experience suggests refinements which could not have been imagined until certain initial steps had been taken. Neither are the techniques suggested here likely to be the ultimate refinement; they may well prove quite naive in the light of future experience.

The scoring method proposed here has the advantages that it appears to deal more adequately with certain kinds of data, eliminating the need for subjective judgements involving essentially non-resolvable questions, and makes possible the application of a single scoring convention to all tests. Even if an investigator does not agree that similarities should be based on "negative" results, this convention will be useful in scoring many tests where negativity is not clear cut or quantitative data are involved. We feel quite strongly—for reasons outlined earlier—that quantitative tests, or those dependent on the presence of another property, should be included only when they can be made to apply to all the strains included in a particular study.

We have tried only to indicate that our reasons for proposing these modifications are not altogether illogical. Their true tests will be that of experience, and their justification (if any) will be that they yield superior results. In the paper which follows (Beers *et al.*, 1962) we have compared the proposed modified methods with other methods, and the results appear encouraging. It is to be hoped that other investigators will test them also. Fortunately the scoring system is such that comparisons will be relatively easy; data need only be re-scored and submitted to the computer program already in use.

There is relatively little practical advantage to be gained at present by using distance rather than similarity as our primary parameter. On theoretical grounds, however, D would appear to be the preferable measure of relationships between organisms, and its advantages should become more apparent as larger quantitites of data become available for comparison.

Our final remarks, concerning the application of computer techniques to diagnosis, are of course premature. Although it may be useful in some instances to compute *P* values as a means of securing descriptions of groups of organisms encountered in individual studies, there are not nearly enough quantitative data available at present about enough taxa to make feasible any attempts to program a diagnostic scheme. Nevertheless, this must be regarded as a legitimate objective for computer taxonomists. The sooner techniques are devised and adopted for dealing with any unsatisfatctory aspects of present scoring schemes, the sooner may we expect to gather enough useful data to make possible the ultimate step.

References

Beers, R. J., Fisher, J., Megraw, S. & Lockhart, W. R. (1962). A comparison of methods for computer taxonomy. *J. gen. Microbiol.* **28**, 641.

Bojalil, L. F. & Cerbón, J. (1961). Taxonomic analysis of non-pigmented, rapidly growing mycobacteria. *J. Bact.* **81**, 338.

Colwell, R. R. & Liston, J. (1961). Taxonomic relationships among the pseudomonads. *J. Bact.* **82**, 1.

Finney, D. J., Hazlewood, T. & Smith, M. J. (1955). Logarithms to base 2. *J. gen. Microbiol.* **12**, 222.

Gilardi, E., Hill, L. R., Turri, M. & Silvestri, L. G. (1960). Quantitative methods in the systematics of Actinomycetales. I. *G. Microbiol.* **8**, 203.

Hill, L. R. (1959). The Adansonian classification of the staphylococci. *J. gen. Microbiol.* **20**, 277.

Hill, L. R., Turri, M., Gilardi, E. & Silvestri, L. G. (1961). Quantitative methods in the systematics of Actinomycetales. II. *G. Microbiol.* **9**, 56.

Lysenko, O. & Sneath, P. H. A. (1959). The use of models in bacterial classification. *J. gen. Microbiol.* **20**, 284.

Rogers, D. J. & Tanimoto, T. T. (1960). A computer program for classifying plants. *Science,* **132**, 1115.

Sneath, P. H. A. (1957*a*). Some thoughts on bacterial classification. *J. gen. Microbiol.* **17**, 184.

Sneath, P. H. A. (1957*b*). The application of computers to taxonomy. *J. gen. Microbiol.* **17**, 201.

Sneath, P. H. A. & Cowan, S. T. (1958). An electrotaxonomic survey of bacteria. *J. gen. Microbiol.* **19**, 551.

Talbot, J. M. & Sneath, P. H. A. (1960). A taxonomic study of *Pasteurella septica,* especially of strains isolated from human sources. *J. gen Microbiol.* **22**, 303.

Methods in Systematic Research

Charles B. Heiser, Jr.

Once upon a time there was a large family who lived deep in the woods in a far off place. They were taxonomists and they were very, very poor. Since this was in the days before the Great Society, the oldest boy of the family decided that he would have to go out into the world to make his fortune. As was customary and proper, his father had a talk with him before he left. There was, he said, in a kingdom some distance away a great castle in which were imprisoned three beautiful princesses whose names it was rumored were the True Species, the True Classification, and the True Phylogeny. The father warned his son that there were many dangers involved—not only were there fierce dragons along the way but the castle wall was covered with man eating vines (*Drosera anthropophagica*) and the trees in the garden of the court (*Pyrus amnesiaca*) had fruits that would make a man forget his quest. However, it was said that anyone who rescued the princesses would possess not only the kingdom and all its riches but the three princesses for his wives. The impending dangers did not deter the son, for the rewards that would be his were great. Armed with his plant press, his dissecting scope, and lots of ambition, he set out to make his mark in the world.

After a year with no word from the first son, the second son went to his father to request permission to make the same journey. He had, he said, been working and studying hard so that he now felt himself capable of rescuing the princesses. With some misgivings the father wished him well and bade him goodbye. So arming himself as had the first son with the addition of a compound miscroscope, he set out upon his way. Reports filtered back that he was fighting gallantly, for many had seen his scalpel bloody with acetocarmine. But after another year when nothing more had been heard, the next in the line, twins, decided it was time for them to try their luck. After lengthy deliberations, they decided that their brothers were not as wise as they were, so they decided to try a different approach. The one took several rabbits and hypodermic needles, while the other armed himself with pipettes and paper; and it must be said that this paraphernalia diverted considerable suspicion from their true mission.

The fifth son, although still quite young, couldn't stand to wait a year before setting out himself. He knew that his brothers were all making a mistake. The way to conquer the castle was simply a matter of numbers.

Reprinted by permission of the author and publisher from *BioScience, 16:* 31–34, 1966.

So armed with great confidence and a computer—which it must be admitted was a bit difficult to carry—he boldly set forth.

Now it happened that when the father was telling his son of the marvelous Kingdom of Truth, a cousin had overheard the conversation. He was not a taxonomist, nor for that matter a biologist, at all—but a philosopher, and he decided that he could win the princesses with no weapon at all except his brain. However, it must be noted that he started out in a completely different direction from that of the sons and never reached the castle.

How many more children the old man has I do not know but word is that another son, Daniel Neill Alonozo, has also left home, and there are some it is said who expect D.N.A, as he is called, to conquer all.

Unfortunately, or perhaps fortunately, the ending of this story has been lost but various authors have attempted to supply one. Some of the more optimistic had the sons joining forces at the castle and waging a successful joint campaign; others have it that the sons met attractive peasant girls in a nearby village and, thinking they were the princesses, settled down to a fairly happy family life with them. The version that they were all turned into frogs I don't like at all.

Now this fairy tale doesn't have much to do with the logic and philosophy of taxonomy except for the reference to the True Species, the True Classification, and the True Phylogeny. It should be made clear the topic under consideration here is *taxonomy proper* and not *methodological taxonomy*. The former deals with organisms and the latter with philosophical issues (Gregg, 1954). One may speak, however, of the logic and philosophy of taxonomy proper, and in recent years a number of authors have touched on these subjects. The book by Simpson (1961) I would certainly list here as a most important contribution, as are the many contributions of Mayr (1964, 1965a, 1965b); I did not see the last paper until after this had been written. Botanists have not been as energetic as the zoologists in expressing their opinions on the subject, but attention should be called to the talks of Constance (1964) and Rollins (1965) as well as to the textbook of Davis and Heywood (1963). Although the philosophy of taxonomy, as I am defining it, had been well expressed before the advent of numerical taxonomy, it is perhaps this development, more than any other, that has stimulated a re-examination of the whole basis of taxonomy as is evident from several of the papers cited above and the symposium held in England last year (Heywood and McNeill, 1964). Certainly biochemical taxonomy has not had the same sort of impact, for it has simply given the taxonomist more characters on which he can base his classification. However, in the long run, it may be that this will be far more significant than any of the contributions of the numercial taxonomists except for the use of the computer.

The taxonomic process obviously involves the organization or arrangement of organisms into species and then the grouping of species into higher and higher groups. A vast amount of this has been done and it is agreed, I believe, that we have a general classification which serves as a useful information-retrieval device (a phrase, however, that wasn't used until recently). There is some concern as to whether the system or systems now in use can be improved. Should a classification aim at being phylogenetic insofar as possible or strictly phenetic, or should a compromise of some sort be effected? I don't intend to try to discuss all these issues but I would like to examine the taxonomic process—or what I think is the basic method of operation of taxonomists today—and I shall confine myself to the lower classification.

After the group for study has been selected, the investigator studies individual specimens, and he works mostly or entirely with morphological characters; the number of these that are used, as Mayr has pointed out, depends upon the patience of the investigator. Some people have emphasized that the taxonomist pays special attention to resemblances, while others have expressed the view that he is chiefly looking for differences—obviously he does both. In looking at characters the investigator is usually influenced by the literature, for previous work has already identified many of the available characters. However, he may find that some of these need reinterpretation and re-evaluation; some, for example, may simply represent ecological modifications; and, of course, he searches for new characters. This process of character selection, rejection, and weighting by taxonomists is one of the great mysteries to some nontaxonomists and to beginning taxonomists, and the latter sometimes ask why we can't have written guides. Part of the answer to this is simply that what may prove to be good specific characters in one group of species may be of no value as specific characters in another group, and what may be a subspecific character in one group of species may be a generic character in another group. Although, for what should be obvious reasons, there is no reason why chemical, cytological, and behavioural characteristics cannot be used, this does not mean that morphological characters will cease to be of great importance.

Following the study of characters, or frequently more or less at the same time, the taxonomist begins a grouping process or clustering, to use the term of the numerical taxonomist. The groups may represent races, species, or even larger units. This grouping of individuals is done according to character correlation and, as Simpson has pointed out, is statistical in principle whether or not numbers are actually employed. It should be mentioned that in this process both geographical distribution and ecological preference are taken into account.

Further analysis decides on the ranking to be given to the various groups of taxa. Although I don't intend to get involved in a discussion of species definitions, which has already been the subject of many interesting, if sometimes rather fruitless, symposia, I would like to point out that an increasing number of taxonomists in the last decade have attempted to employ a "biological species" definition in their work. In plant groups this has led to many practical difficulties as was well illustrated in the papers presented at the Urbana AIBS meetings by Theodore Mosquim and William Grant in the symposium on Intraspecific Variation in Angio-sperms. We may assume that if we have conspicuous morphological gaps between populations or groups of populations that these exist because of failure to interbreed. A problem may remain as to whether allopatric populations represent species or subspecies. If breeding experiments are carried out, these may determine whether allopatric populations are potentially interbreeding, but even if they are, there may still be some problems as to whether they should be called species or subspecies. I should add that there are some groups, particularly in polyploid and apomictic complexes, where compromises are nearly always called for in order to recognize species.

The species can then be grouped into sections or subgenera, this again depending on correlation of character combinations. It may be that no major groupings of species are possible. Sometimes a single character is used; this may admittedly result in quite artificial groups, but can sometimes be defended on the grounds of convenience.

Following this, or again more or less concurrently, an evolutionary interpretation may be attempted and phylogenetic conclusions drawn. The evolutionary interpretation may or may not involve some changes in classification above this species level. It should be noted that the classification is usually far along or actually completed before phylogenetic conclusions are drawn. Thus the criticism that phylogeny plays havoc with taxonomy, an argument advanced by some numerical taxonomist, hardly appears valid.

It is to be noted that I have not mentioned "types," the reason being that types have nothing to do with taxonomy except for the names used. The application of names to species is important but not a biological matter and has nothing to do with classification. Perhaps the taxonomist should eliminate the word "type" from his vocabulary since it is a source of misunderstanding to nontaxonomists. For the purpose of nomenclature the "type" method prevents chaos and certainly one can't propose its elimination.

Although the fairy tale may have seemed to indicate otherwise, I see nothing really incompatible in the method I have just outlined as far as biosystematics or biochemical taxonomy is concerned. The methods of these subdisciplines may be used along with the more or less traditional procedures in an early stage of the taxonomic process. It should be realized, however, that frequently the biosystematist or biochemical taxonomist selects groups for investigation that have already been studied by the traditional comparative morphological method. Not only do the more recent workers have the benefit of new characters but also they usually have more material if they choose to study museum specimens. Numerical taxonomy, as now generally advocated, is another matter. One of the basic differences between numerical and nonnumerical taxonomy, it seems to me, is that the nonnumerical taxonomist is faced with making decisions—both as to choice of characters and to limits of categories—whereas numerical taxonomy has removed all this anxiety. It should be noted in passing that numerical taxonomy produces results essentially similar to those already secured by traditional methods. One exception, at least in part, is provided by a recent study of *Solanum* (Heiser *et al.*, 1965).

I would like to use various taxonomic treatments of *Artemisia* to illustrate certain points. This genus of the Compositae is generally recognized as a difficult one. In 1916, it was treated for the North American Flora by Rydberg (1916) who recognized 122 species. Seven years later it was monographed by Hall and Clements (1923) who accepted only 29 species. This discrepancy in the number of species recognized by different workers is sometimes used to discredit taxonomy, but I feel unjustly so. The disagreements as to the number of species are not as serious as the nontaxonomist might suppose. Taxonomists recognized Rydberg as a splitter. He had a keen eye and almost anything that appeared different he recognized with a binomial; and, of course, some of his new species are, in fact, accepted today. The extreme splitter, fortunately, is disappearing as a result of a kind of natural selection—that is, those professors who have a temperate species concept are producing most of the students who are becoming practicing taxonomists. Although it is true that the taxonomist has to take into account the work of earlier generations of taxonomists, quite unlike the situation in most other branches of biology, it is hardly fair to hold taxonomists today responsible for the work of the past. The emphasis on this point is made in particular reference to a section on "The Ills of Modern Taxonomy" by Sokal and Sneath (1963) in their recent book.

My selection of *Artemisia* as an example was not primarily to contrast the treatments of Rydberg with those of Hall and Clements but to contrast the latter with more recent works in the group. In 1946, David Keck (1946) brought out a study of the *Artemisia vulgaris* section. This section in which Rydberg included 54 species was treated as a single species with 15 subspecies by Hall and Clements; Keck recognized 11 species. A comparison of his treatment with that of Hall and Clements is shown in Table 1. I call particular attention to the fact that the Old World *A. vulgaris* is shown to have a different basic chromosome number from the North American species. A second recent treatment of *Artemisia* species is Ward's study (1953) of the section *Seriphidium* in which he

TABLE 1

Comparison of Two Treatments of Certain Taxa of *Artemisia*

Keck, 1946	Hall and Clements, 1923
1. A. vulgaris n = 8	A. vulgaris ssp. typica
2. A. michauxiana	A. vulgaris ssp. discolor
3. A. longifolia n = 18	A. vulgaris ssp. longifolia
4. A. serrata n = 18	A. vulgaris ssp. serrata
5. A. caruthii n = 9	A. vulgaris ssp. wrightii
6. A. ludoviciana ssp. typica n = 18	A. vulgaris ssp. ludoviciana
	A. vulgaris ssp. ganaphalodes
A. ludoviciana ssp. sulcata	
A. ludoviciana ssp. albula	
A. ludoviciana ssp. candicans	A. vulgaris ssp. candicans
A. ludoviciana ssp. incompta n = 18	A. vulgaris ssp. flodmanii
A. ludoviciana ssp. mexicana	A. vulgaris ssp. mexicana
A. ludoviciana ssp. redolens	A. vulgaris ssp. redolens
7. A. lindleyana	A. vulgaris ssp. lindleyana
8. A. suksdorfii n = 9	A. vulgaris ssp. litoralis
9. A. douglasiana n = 27	A. vulgaris ssp. heterophylla
10. A. prescottiana	
11. A. tilesii ssp. typica	A. vulgaris ssp. tilesii
A. tilesii ssp. unalaschcensis n = 27	

TABLE 2

Comparison of Two Treatments of Certain Taxa of *Artemisia*

Ward, 1953	Hall and Clements, 1923
1. A. bigelovii n = 9	A. bigelovii
2. A. tridentata ssp. tridentata n = 9, 18	A. tridentata ssp. typica (in part)
A. tridentata ssp. parishii n = 18	A. tridentata ssp. parishii
3. A. arbuscula ssp. arbuscula n = 9, 18	A. tridentata ssp. arbuscula
A. arbuscula ssp. nova n = 9, 18	A. tridentata ssp. nova
4. A. tripartita = 9, 18	A. tridentata ssp. trifida
5. A. cana ssp. cana n = 9, 18	A. cana
A. cana ssp. bolanderi n = 9	A. tridentata ssp. bolanderi
6. A. rothrockii n = 18, 27, 36	A. tridentata ssp. rothrockii
7. A. rigida n = 9, 18	A. rigida
8. A. pygmaea n = 9	A. pygmaea
9. A. palmeri n = 9	A. palmeri

recognized nine species as opposed to the six of Clements and Hall (Table 2). However, the disagreement in the number of species recognized is not as serious as that between Rydberg and the other workers. If one refers to the tables, it will be seen that there is fairly general agreement as to the taxa but not on the categories to be employed. Thus, in a sense, the classification of Hall and Clements as well as that of Keck and Ward is biologically sound. The more recent treatments are probably more realistic as perhaps is indicated by the fact that the species concept of Keck and Ward has been accepted in most recent floristic treatments.

As I have indicated above, it is not really fair to make comparisons between monographs that have been done a quarter of a century apart, for the more recent investigators not only have the advantage of more material but frequently new tools as well—in the example cited, the use of chromosome numbers. The great contribution of Keck was to show that the Old World *Artemisia vulgaris* has a different basic chromosome number from the New World species and also that the North American species form a polyploid series. Thus a single character, although in a way a very special sort of character—chromosome number—has proved of great significance. In all probability the difference in chromosome number confers partial or complete genetic isolation between certain of these species.

It should be added, however, that chromosome number, like other characters, may be of only limited value in other groups. This is partially true of Ward's study. Some of the species in section *Seriphidium,* as treated by Ward, included diploid and tetraploid races and one includes a hexaploid as well. There are some who maintain that since such chromosome races are generally genetically isolated they should be maintained as distinct species. Ward did not do so for the logical reason that he could not find morphological differences to distinguish them.

The studies of Keck and Ward are not complete biosystematic studies. We do not know from experimental work whether or not the species are genetically isolated. Such tests would be of interest and certainly would contribute to our understanding of the evolution of the group. But I am rash enough to predict that such a study would not result in any drastic altering of the present taxonomy even though it could be shown that fertile hybrids could be obtained artificially between some of the species. While I am playing the role of prophet, we might ask what biochemical or numerical taxonomic studies would contribute to the taxonomy of *Artemisia.* It is possible that the former might help in distinguishing the different chromosome races—this, of course, might depend on whether they are autoploids or alloploids. Then again it might not. In some groups chromatographic analysis has revealed much concerning the origin of polyploids, but in others (in studies that are usually never published) it has contributed little. A numerical study, on the other hand, might well reveal the major taxa in the group which are already recognized and whether these would be categorized as species or subspecies would depend on where the investigator chose to draw his phenon lines for taxa.

This second part of this article is somewhat like the first in that it has no ending. There are, however, a few random observations to which I would like to call attention. It may seem to some that taxonomy has changed little since the time of Linnaeus. This is not true, although changes have been slow. Part of the reason for this is that it has taken a long time for other disciplines to reach the level of usefulness to taxonomy. Thus cytology and genetics did not become useful until the 30's and only recently has biochemistry become important. It should be pointed out that much taxonomic work remains to be done that doesn't necessarily involve either cytogenetics or biochemistry. After more than 200 years we still lack monographs of many groups and floras and faunas of many regions. Perhaps the computer will help to speed up the work. Much of taxonomic work is dull and tedious. It is to be hoped that modern data processing devices can eliminate much of the nonbiological work, such as the time consuming search of the literature involved in taxonomic research.

References

Constance, Lincoln (1964). Systematic botany-an unending synthesis. Taxon, 8: 257–273.

Davis, P. H., and V. H. Heywood (1963). Principles of Angiosperm Taxonomy. Oliver and Boyd, Edinburgh. 556 p.

Gregg, John R. (1954). The Language of Taxonomy. Columbia University Press, New York. 70 p.

Hall, Harvey M., and Frederick E. Clements. (1923). The phylogenetic method in taxonomy. Carnegie Inst. Wash. Publ., 326: 1–355.

Heiser, Charles B., Jorge Soria, and Donald Burton. (1965). A numerical taxonomic study of *Solanum* species and hybrids. Amer. Nat. (in press).

Heywood, V. H., and J. McNeill (eds.) (1964). Phenetic and phylogenetic classification. Systematics Assoc. Publ. #6, London, 164 p.

Keck, David D. (1946). A revision of the *Artemisia vulgaris* complex in North America. Proc. Calif. Acad. Sci., **25**: 421–468.

Mayr, Ernst. (1964). The new systematics. In C. A. Leone (ed.) Taxonomic Biochemistry and Serology. Ronald Press, New York. p. 13–32.

Mayr, Ernst. (1965a). Classification and phylogeny. Amer. Zool., 5: 165–174.

Mayr, Ernst. (1965b). Numerical phenetics and taxonomic theory. Systematic Zool., 14: 73–97.

Rollins, Reed C. (1965). On the basis of biological classification. Taxon, 14: 1–6.

Rydberg, P. A. (1916). *Artemisia* (and) *Artemisiastrum.* In North American Flora, 34: 244–285.

Simpson, George G. (1961). Principles of Animal Taxonomy. Columbia University Press, New York. 247 p.

Sokal, Robert R., and P. H. A. Sneath. (1963). Principles of Numerical Taxonomy. W. H. Freeman and Co., San Francisco. 359 p.

Ward, George H. (1953). *Artemisia,* section *Seriphidium,* in North America, a cytotaxonomic study. Contr. Dudley Herb. (Stanford Univ.), 4: 155–205.

2 / Systematics

Systematics in its literal meaning is classification by systems. In the nineteenth century the purpose of biological systematics was to achieve a phylogenetic system of classification of the living world according to the principle of descent. Taxonomy—the study of the principles underlying phylogenetic relationships—did not develop until the twentieth century. In recent years, however, the terms *systematics* and *taxonomy* have frequently been used as if they were synonomous and, therefore, interchangeable. This is not so. Taxonomy, as has been illustrated in the previous section, is a study of *principles.* Systematics is a study of *phylogeny*—the origin and inter-relationships of groups of living and fossil organisms.

In a paper dealing with a specialized fossil group, the British geologist and systematist P.C. Sylvester-Bradley presents an analysis of the modern treatment applied to such systematic phenomena as *radiation, divergence,* and *similarity.*

Some 25 years ago there developed the *New Systematics,* whose tenets are incorporated in a classical work of that title edited by Julian Huxley. The distinguished American systematist Ernst Mayr describes the new systematics, and current approaches to the problems of classification of birds, from the species level to higher categories. In this paper Mayr relates classification to the modern studies on the taxonomy of populations illustrated in the previous section.

The Taxonomic Treatment of Phylogenetic Patterns in Time and Space, with Examples from the Ostracoda

P. C. Sylvester-Bradley

1. The Scientific Basis of Taxonomy

Taxonomy can only be regarded as a science if it employs scientific methods. According to Popper (1959) the crucial test of whether investigation is scientific or not depends on the part that speculation plays. A scientist erects a working hypothesis, and proceeds to subject the hypothesis to tests, which may be experimental or observational.

During the past few years some of the basic concepts of taxonomy have been discussed in the pages of *Systematic Zoology* (e.g. Bigelow, 1958,

Reprinted by permission of the author and publisher from the Systematics Association Publication 4, *Taxonomy and Geography,* 1962, pp. 119–33.

1959; Bader, 1958; Kiriakoff, 1959; Myers, 1960). In this discussion Bigelow has challenged the assumption that *similarity* corresponds with *recency of common ancestry*. In a series of able papers Cain and Harrison have dealt with the philosophical aspects of rather similar problems (see especially Cain and Harrison, 1960; also Cain, 1958, 1959; Cain and Harrison, 1958). One of the main arguments has hinged on the degree to which similarity reflects consanguinity in the sense of 'recency of common ancestry'. Pre-evolutionary taxonomic schemes attempted to group together in one taxon organisms which shared common morphological characters. Such morphological characters have been called 'taxobases' by Cox (1960), and a classification based on them can be called 'typological'. Post-evolutionary taxonomy, on the other hand, groups together in the same taxon organisms which share a common ancestor. As Cox has clearly shown, if all readily observable morphological characters in a particular line of descent were undergoing continuous change, no species in that line would share a common character. Yet on phylogenetic grounds they would be grouped in a single taxon. Cox goes on to suggest that the discerning taxonomist will attempt to detect morphological characters which remained relatively stable during evolution though others were changing, and these stable characters can then be used as measures of similarity; they are suitable for choice as 'taxobases' in an evolutionary classification.

There are those who prefer their classification to be free of phylogenetic assumptions and based entirely on similarity as in pre-evolutionary times. That such a viewpoint is not confined to those who deal with organisms without a fossil history is shown by Weller (1949). However, others (e.g. Cox, 1960; Simpson, 1961; Wright, 1950) believe that a phylogenetic classification is the only one which can become 'universal and permanent'. The contrast in the two viewpoints is interesting. A classification based on similarity may be arbitrary, but it can be expressed in objective terms. A classification based on phylogeny is a revelation of natural facts, but the 'revelation' must, even when supported by fossil evidence, always be subjective, and is often wildly speculative. In the former case the classification itself is always in part arbitrary and subjective, but the means of arriving at it are objectve; in the latter case the classification is objective, but the means are subjective.

The method that most practising taxonomists adopt passes through stages. First, a typological classification is constructed which is based on similarities (taxobases); gradually this is modified in the light of phylogenetic discoveries. A fully phylogenetic classification is an ideal at which to aim. The typological classification is a starting-point from which to work. A 'working' classification is a compromise between the two. In constructing such a compromise the taxonomist must erect a phylogenetic scheme as a working hypothesis. Such phylogenies are hypotheses amenable to tests in the manner of all scientific hypotheses. There are two basic assumptions. The first is the postulate that two organisms are related to each other as ancestor and descendant; the second, that two contemporary organisms have arisen from a common ancestor. The two postulates depend on the two basic processes of evolution, *phylogenesis* (modification during descent) and *cladogenesis* (branching of the phyletic line). In testing hypotheses of cladogenesis, the taxonomist faces problems posed by the interaction of evolution, migration, and time. In postulating a common ancestor, one must necessarily also postulate divergence, and therefore invoke phylogenesis in one or both of two branches that spring from the ancestor. The degree of divergence from the ancestor in each branch will also inevitably differ in both direction and degree; and the discontinuity that arises between the branches (and that is the essential feature of cladogenesis) seems almost always to be accompanied by spatial separation. Consequently an investigation into the occurrence of cladogenesis must penetrate into the geological record, and must trace the migratory routes followed through time and space by the two evolutionary lines or 'clades', as Huxley (1959) calls them. It is the purpose of the present paper to examine the observational tests that can be brought to bear on the hypotheses of cladogenesis that are implicit in all taxonomic schemes that claim to be phylogenetic.

2. Cladogenesis as a Process

Current evolutionary theory suggests that cladogenesis takes place according to a certain pattern (Sylvester-Bradley, 1960). According to this theory, all branches arise in the first place from a single population (gamodeme) of a single species. The sequence of events results from the action of changing selection pressure on a population that fluctuates in size and migrates. There are four stages in the process (Fig. 1 and Table I). A population that is stable in size and occupies a constant environment will normally be subject to a stabilizing selection pressure; this keeps variation in check, and favours the norm, already selected for the environment in question. The first stage in cladogenesis is initiated when

TABLE I
Phases of Cladogenesis

Phase	Selection Pressure	Type of Phylogenesis
1. Eruption	Reduced	Typogenesis
2. Isolation and Reticulation	Disruptive	Anagenesis
3. Divergence	Directional	Orthogenesis
4. Stabilization	Stabilizing	Stasigenesis

for some reason this stablizing selection pressure slackens off. Numbers go up and the population spreads and covers a wider ecological range of habitats than previously. Simultaneously morphological variation is increased. During this phase, when variation is rife, new morphological types arise and these may be pre-adapted to the new environments encountered as the population spreads over a wider territory. This is one of the ways in which new taxa can arise discontinuously and can be referred to as *typogenesis.*

The second phase starts as soon as numbers build up to an optimum beyond which heavy selection pressures are reimposed. This is the stage of isolation. Selection is now disruptive—it will vary over the whole territory of the population, and the single population will split up into discontinuous gamodemes, each being subjected to pressures in a different direction. But periods of isolation, with division into subspecies, are followed by periods of expansion, with hybridization at the subspecific level. Thus the phylogenetic pattern is, during this phase, a network,

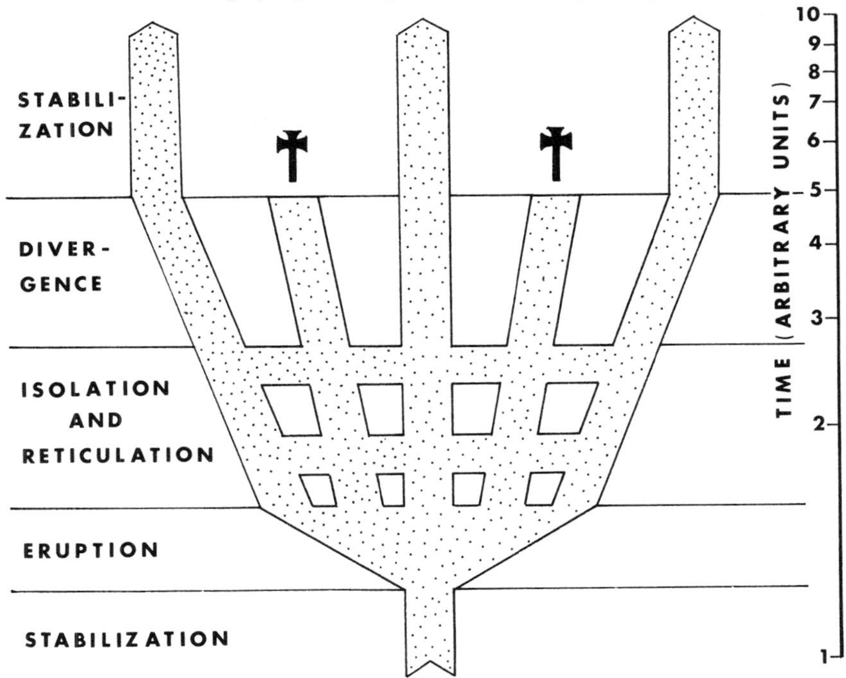

Fig. 1. The typical phylogenetic pattern in cladogenesis. Four phases succeed each other. In the eruptive phase the ancestral species increases in numbers and extends its area of occupation. The phase of isolation is prolonged by periods of subspecific reticulation. Of the five clades that survive this phase, two become extinct during the phase of divergence. The three survivors persist into the future. Each phase is of increasing length, as indicated by the time scale, which is plotted on a logarithmic scale, though with units of arbitrary and unspecified length. For further explanations see text and Table I.

and the phase is not only one of isolation, but also of reticulation. Hybrid swarms may arise, and the consequent increase in variation will contribute to that already characteristic of the eruptive phase. Subspecific reticulation can therefore be considered as an integral part of phase 2. This is the active, progressive evolutionary stage, and proceeds by *anagenesis.* For if pre-adapted characters are selected by the demands of a new environment, rapid modification will ensue, and new functional grades may be achieved (Huxley, 1959).

The third phase begins as soon as isolation is complete, and reticulation at an end. Selection is now directional. Evolutionary trends, initiated by anagenesis, are continued by *orthogenesis* (using this term in its original sense for steady evolutionary adaptation along trend-lines; see Sylvester-Bradley, 1960). Orthogenesis is the most common phylogenetic pattern revealed by palaeontology. At one time mysterious forces were invoked by palaeontologists to account for it, but it is now generally agreed that a directional selection pressure must inevitably result in a directional response.

Eventually phase 4 is reached. The various branches have become adapted to their new environments. Often specialization has been extreme, and in this case a majority of clades are likely to become extinct; a few may survive. Selection will be stable, evolution will be by *stasigenesis.* Of course, any of these branches may subsequently undergo a further eruption; cladogenesis may then take place again.

It is always possible that cladogenesis will result in only two surviving clades, but often this is not so. A consideration, for example, of the post-Pleistocene history of terrestrial animals in the northern hemisphere shows a general pattern that is followed alike by vertebrates and invertebrates. A continental species enters the phase of eruption as the climate ameliorates, and spreads over a wide area. Then conditions worsen, the continental species retracts, and isolated gamodemes are left on the periphery, each of which subsequently diverges to form a distinct subspecies. The continental form often remains controlled by stablizing selection, and alters less from its ancestors than do the marginal subspecies. Thus the faunas of the Hebridean and other off-shore islands of Britain are characterized by endemic subspecies of mammals and birds that can be supposed to have arisen in this way.

Although it is therefore true to say that cladogenesis most often seems to give rise to more than two descendant branches, yet it is evident that the degree of separation effected is very varied. Extreme cases are formed in the juxtaposition of circumstances that gave rise to the explosive bursts of evolution evident in the fauna and flora of volcanic archipelagos like Hawaii and the Galapagos, or in continental lakes like Baikal or those of the East African rift valleys. Subspeciation in many British birds (e.g. the wrens) and butterflies (e.g. the Swallowtail) is much less dramatic. Yet the difference seems one of degree, not of kind.

3. The Taxonomic Treatment of Radiation

One of the characteristics of the phylogenetic pattern discovered by palaeontology is that many major taxa start in evolutionary bursts that much resemble the picture of cladogenesis given above. This pattern, however, is characteristic not only of taxa of specific level; if anything, genera and families seem to originate in batches even more often than do species, and it is this phenomenon which has been designated 'adaptive radition'. The observational evidence for such a pattern (much of which has been documented by Rensch, 1959) is not conclusive, but it is suggestive. Stasigenesis is to be postulated if it can be demonstrated that a batch of related taxa can be traced back into the geological past without morphological modification greater than that already existing between members of the group. Cladogenesis must, of course, have occurred at some time previous to the first appearance of the individual clades. This self-evident conclusion is of great importance when one draws up a taxonomic scheme in which the concept of recency plays some part. It can be illustrated by an example drawn from the Ostracoda, which have been the subject of a recent volume of the *Treatise on Invertebrate Paleontology* (Moore, 1961), and in the *Osnovӯ paleontologii*, the Russian equivalent of the *Treatise* (Chernysheav, 1960); they have undergone taxonomic revision in both of these.

Three of the first genera of Ostracoda to be described were *Cypris* (1776), *Cythere* (1785), and *Bairdia* (1844). The first is freshwater in habit, the other two marine. Subsequently families were based on the first two, although they were considered sufficiently close to warrant placing them in the same suborder. Somewhat later Sars (1888) separated *Bairdia* from the Cyprididae, and proposed a new family, Bairdiidae, for its reception. He was not followed by many workers, however, who preferred to retain *Bairdia* in the family Cyprididae; indeed Sars himself recanted, and in 1923 reduced his family to subfamily rank, and placed it within the Cyprididae.

Nowadays palaeontologists have promoted all three of the families under discussion to superfamily rank. Many still prefer to regard *Cypris* and *Bairdia* as members of the same superfamily, Cypridacea. Others separate the Bairdiacea as a distinct superfamily. Representatives of the three families are to be found Recent, and on the basis of comparative morphology (or, to use the terminology of Cain and Harrison, 1960, in 'phenetic' terms) *Cypris* is closer to *Bairdia* than either is to *Cythere*. But the geological ranges of the three genera are very different; *Bairdia* is the longest-lived ostracod genus know. The type-species is from the Carboniferous of Ireland, and other species have been recorded from as far back as the Ordovician. The Palaozoic members of the genus have been compared with the Recent, and no difference worthy of generic distinction could be found (Sylvester-Bradley, 1950). *Bairdia* provides a fine example of stasigenesis. The family is in Recent seas represented by only four genera (*Bairdia, Anchistrocheles, Triebelina,* and *Bythocypris;* there seems doubt about the validity of *Bairdoppilata*—see Reyment and Reyment, 1959). In Palaeozoic times, however, this was quite different, and *Bairdia* was just one clade of radiations which gave rise to as many as fifteen genera (Fig. 2), and recently Kollmann (1960) has described two Triassic genera. *Cythere* and *Cypris* both have origins in the Tertiary, and both are the product of Tertiary radiations. In the case of *Cypris,* this radiation seems to have been the second major one in the history of the superfamily. Thus the *Treatise* (Moore, 1961) records, as the outcome of the second radiation, 47 genera of the Cypridacea known fossil in the Tertiary (67 genera are known Recent only). The first radiation took place in Upper Jurassic and Lower Cretaceous time, and gave rise to 24 genera. Only 7 genera are known from the earlier Mesozoic (Palaeozoic freshwater ostracods are not yet known well enough to make their reference to the superfamily reliable). The Cytheracea, on the other hand, were already well represented in Jurassic times, and the fauna is at the moment being intensively investigated in many countries. Most of the Jurassic genera seem to be different from those in the Cretaceous, though many of the Cretaceous genera survive into the Tertiary. Descriptive research has not yet proceeded far enough to determine the phylogenetic pattern, but it seems certain that it is more complicated than in either of the other groups, and that a whole succession of radiations occurred during Mesozoic and Tertiary time, and that these have not been fully documented in either the *Treatise* or *Osnovȳ.* The first of these radiations seems to have taken place at the close of the Permian (Kashevarova, Mandelstam, and Schneider, in Chernysheva, 1960).

The three genera *Cypris, Cythere,* and *Bairdia* therefore have very different geological histories, and the contrasts of phylogenetic pattern are given in diagrammatic form in Fig. 2. The taxonomic treatment of this situation adopted in the *Treatise* (Moore, 1961) has been to give each branch the rank of superfamily, and to group the superfamilies together in a single suborder, the Podocopina. Perhaps this procedure will be opposed by those who believe the phenetic resemblance between *Cypris* and *Bairdia* should find expression in the classification.

The Podocopina has one other superfamily, newly proposed in the *Treatise,* based on the genus *Darwinula,* which is another long-lived genus, ranging from Triassic (early Mesozoic) to Recent. Previous classifications have placed *Darwinula* in the same superfamily as *Cypris.* The

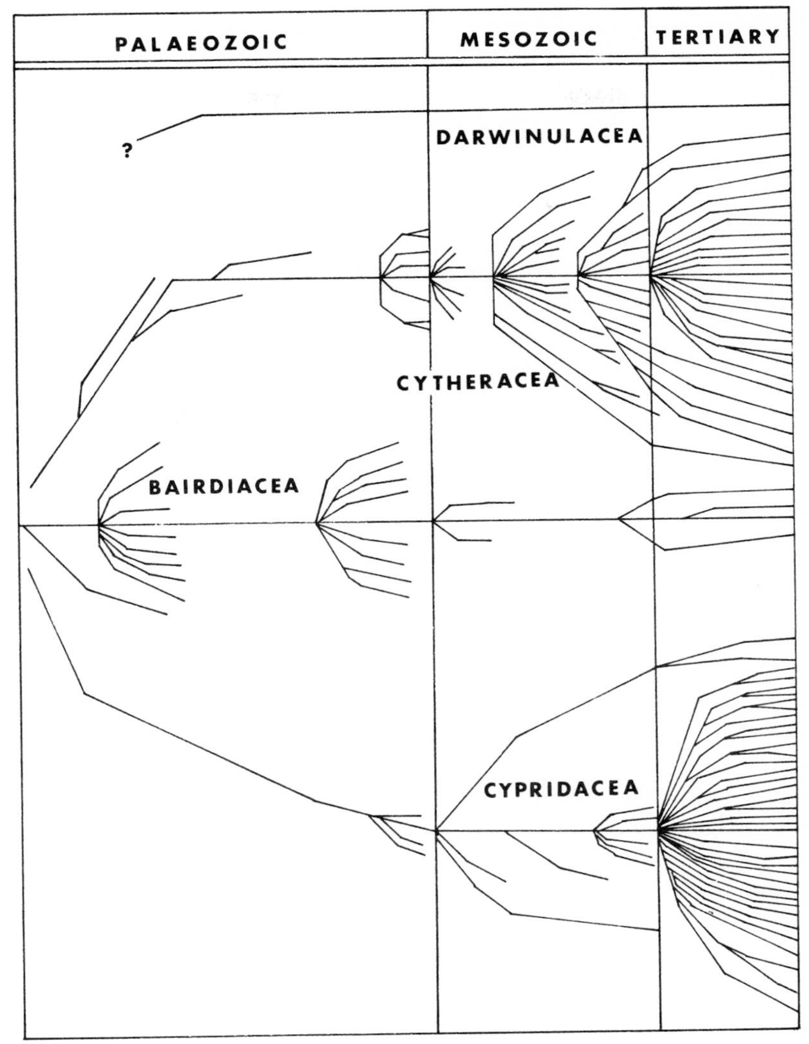

Fig. 2. Diagrammatic representation of phylogenetic patterns within the ostracod suborder Podocopina. Each of the main clades represents a superfamily. The minor clades, produced at each period of radiation, are genera, though only a proportion of those known in the Cytheracea and Cypridacea are indicated. (Data modified from Chernysheva, 1960, and Moore, 1961.)

proposal to separate it as a distinct superfamily becomes almost inevitable, both on phenetic and phylogenetic (or 'cladistic'; see Cain and Harrison, 1960) grounds, once the Bairdiacea are separated from the Cypridacea; indeed, it may have been derived from the Healdiacea rather than from the Bairdiacea (see p. 130 below).

To summarize, the examples illustrate a method of evaluating phylogeny for taxonomic purposes. The method depends on the discovery of sufficient evidence to warrant the postulation and approximate dating of phases of cladogenetic radiation in the geological past.

4. The Taxonomic Treatment of Divergence

In the examples discussed above, there has been little evidence for long-continued evolutionary divergence. The phylogenetic pattern that best fits the palaeontological data is that of Fig. 1, in which a relatively abrupt radiation is succeeded by a long-continued phase of stasigenesis. Each of the three superfamilies can be diagnosed by characters which can be chosen as 'taxobases' and these remain diagnostic throughout their geological history. But, as Cox (1960) has emphasized, this is not the case in all animals. When divergence continues through an appreciable period of geological time, a taxonomic problem must inevitably be created. Diverging clades, when traced back to their common ancestor, will gradually become more and more difficult to diagnose, until they merge. Diverging clades inevitably pose the problem of whether to divide the phylogenetic tree horizontally or vertically. The question has been dealt with lucidly by Simpson (1961, pp. 129 ff.) with special reference to the Carnivora. In the Ostracoda, similar problems are posed in the classification of suborders closely related to those already discussed, and grouped with them in the same order in the *Treatise.* When Sars first grouped *Cythere, Cypris,* and *Bairdia* together in his suborder Podocopa, he also created a special suborder, Platycopa, for the single genus *Cytherella.* Later Müller (1894) thought Sars was mistaken in separating *Cytherella,* and united the two suborders. But Sars (1923) stuck to his guns, and maintained that the phenetic distinction between the two suborders was sound, and Sars has since been followed by most other workers. The suborder Platycopa (or 'Platycopina', as adopted in the *Treatise*) is best characterized by its originally included genus *Cytherella,* although a few other genera have now been described (e.g. *Cytherelloidea, Platella*). *Cytherella* is a long-lived genus, and certainly extends back into the Jurassic where it is often very abundant. At one time it was thought to extend even farther back, and be abundant in the Palaeozoic, but it has been found that these Palaeozoic specimens differ slightly from the true *Cytherella.* It seems that the only difference in the shell is in the form of the muscle scar (Fig. 3, *a* and *b*). This is not a great difference, but it is a constant one and enables us to separate the Palaeozoic specimens as a separate genus, *Cavellina.* It seems natural to include *Cavellina* within the same suborder as *Cytherella* (i.e. the Platycopina), but there are complications. *Cavellina* is accompanied by a host of other genera which it phenetically resembles to a greater or lesser degree. Some of these other genera are close enough to suggest the same family, others the same superfamily, others the same suborder. Apparently we are dealing with a series of radiations which took place in mid-Palaeozoic time, and at first it seems reasonable to group all these forms together in the Platycopina, and to distinguish several superfamilies, but there are two further complications. First, all these Palaeozoic superfamilies share the same muscle scar as *Cavellina,* and they all differ in this respect from *Cytherella* and the other later Cytherellids (Fig. 3). Secondly, a certain number of the Palaeozoic forms show in their shape and ornament a striking likeness to some of the Bairdiacea and Cytheracea that were discussed above. They differ from them in muscle scar and in some other characters (probably in the marginal duplicature), but the characters that they have in common suggest convergence, and this may be due either to a similar phenetic response to a similar environment or to the fact that the clades have at this stage not diverged far from the common ancestor of the order. The two hypotheses need testing against each other. At one time it was thought that the Devonian Ropolenellacea, which resemble in shape Mesozoic and Tertiary Cytheracea, also possessed a similar duplicature, but recent work by Scott (1960) now makes this seem unlikely. But taxonomy can seldom wait for the conclusion of phylogenetic research, and it is necessary to come to some decision as to the classification of these forms before these evolutionary questions can be answered. Three solutions seemed reasonable (see Fig. 4):

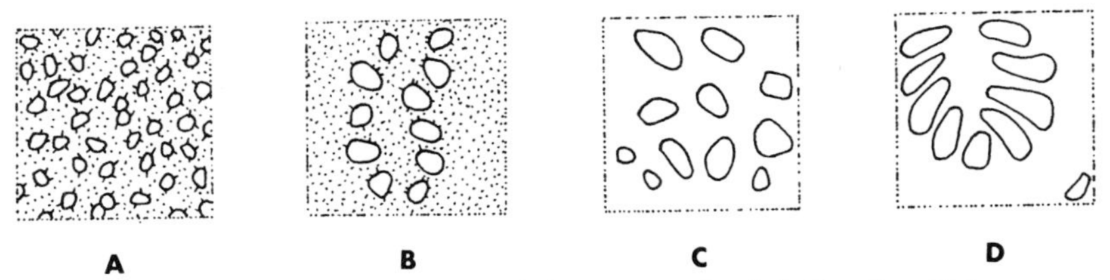

Fig. 3. Muscle-scar patterns of four ostracods: (a) *Cavellina* (aggregate); (b) *Cytherella* (biserial); (c) *Bairdia* (discrete); (d) *Darwinula* (discrete). (Drawn from photographs by E. Triebel.)

(i) all the Palaeozoic superfamilies with aggregate muscle scars can be grouped together with their descendants, the Mesozoic to Recent Cytherellacea, within the suborder Playtycopina (A + B + C of Fig. 4), leaving those with discrete scars (D) in the Podocopina;

(ii) the Palaeozoic superfamilies with aggregate scars can be grouped together in a new suborder (Metacopina; B + C of Fig. 4), leaving their descendants with biserial scars, the Cytherellacea (A), as the sole representatives of the Platycopina, and those with discrete scars (D) as the Podocopina;

(iii) the Cavellinidae (B of Fig. 4) can be separated from the rest of the Palaeozoic forms with aggregate scars (C) and grouped instead with their Mesozoic descendants, the Cytherellacea, as the Platycopina

(A + B); the remainder of the forms with aggregate scars (C) can then either:

(*a*) be united with those which have discrete scars to form the Podocopina (C + D); or

(*b*) be separated to form a new suborder (Metacopina, C) distinct from the Podocopina (D).

The *Treatise* was written by a sizeable team of American and European authors, and all three of the above solutions appealed to different members of the team. The three solutions represent various compromises between 'vertical' and 'horizonal' classifications (cf. Simpson, 1961, fig. 9). The final choice for the *Treatise* (Moore, 1961) was the second, and

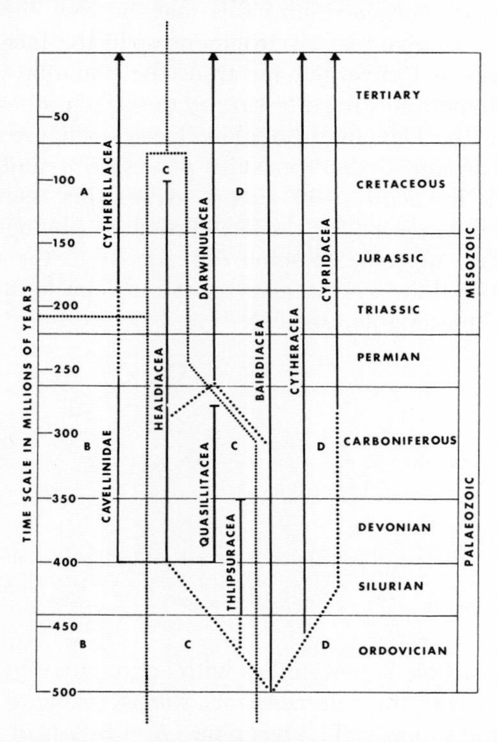

Fig. 4. Classification of superfamilies within the ostracod order Podocopida. Of the various possible groupings into suborders, the *Treatise* (Moore, 1961) group B and C in the Metacopina, leaving A in the Platycopina, D in the Podocopina; the *Osnovy̅* (Chernysheva, 1960) group A and B as the Platycopa, C and D as the Podocopa.

the reasons for this seem important, for they are likely to be common to similar examples in other parts of the animal kingdom. By choosing the second alternative, it was possible to distinguish all three suborders on the basis of the muscle scar. The new suborder (Metacopina), for the Palaeozoic forms related to *Cavellina*, is characterized by an aggregate muscle scar, the Podocopina have a discrete muscle-scar pattern, and in the Platycopina it is biserial (Fig. 3). Certainly the differences of muscle-scar pattern are differences of 'grade' in the sense of Huxley (1959), and discrete scars may have arisen polyphyletically. Nevertheless this solution to the taxonomic problem provides each suborder with an unambiguous diagnosis—that is, with a 'taxobasis'—and this seems to me to be better than adopting any arbitrary rule that prefers a 'vertical' classification to a 'horizontal' one, or vice versa.

Our Russian colleagues, however, have adopted solution No. iii *a* (Chernysheva, 1960). They were influenced in this by their conclusion that the Darwinulidae may have sprung from the Healdiacea. This suggestion seems perfectly sound, for the marginal details of *Darwinula* are reminiscent of those in some of the Healdiids; but the muscle-scar pattern of *Darwinula* is unique; it differs radically from the Healdiacea; perhaps it shows greater resemblance to *Bairdia* than to anything else (see Fig. 3). It may therefore be related to either *Healdia* or to *Bairdia;* present evidence is insufficient to decide between the two hypotheses.

Thus two solutions to the taxonomic problem have been adopted: No. ii in Moore (1961); No. iii *a* in *Chernysheva* (1960). Both have disadvantages. In the former, the Cavellinidae are separated from their acknowledged descendants, the Cytherellacea; in the latter the Cavellinidae are separated from the contemporary Healdiacea, which they very closely resemble.

5. Observational Tests

Cladogenesis introduces discontinuities between the resultant clades. These discontinuities are objective, and it is by their recognition that taxa based on them can claim to be 'natural' rather than arbitrary. Discontinuities such as those that separate clade from clade do not separate successive transients within a clade. But every time cladogenesis further affects a clade, an interruption of a somewhat different kind does occur. The 'node' of a dividing clade would provide a possible non-arbitrary discontinuity for taxonomic recognition *if it were in practice* recognizable. In the preceding paragraphs the Ostracoda have been used to illustrate the general procedure of adapting a taxonomic scheme to a phylogenetic pattern. Implicit in this scheme is the recognition of periods of active cladogenesis, leading to radiation. Only taxa of generic rank and above were considered. But according to the theories of cladogenesis outlined above the process is always initiated at the subspecific level. Phase 1 of Fig. 1 and Table I is at first intraspecific. During phases 2 and 3 divergence may lead to the origin of species, genera, families, or higher taxa, but during phase 1 the common ancestor is a single species, and the isolates of phase 2 are at first subspecies. The evidence for the existence of radiations such as those described above in the Ostracoda is limited to the simultaneous appearance in the geological column of several related genera. Even this evidence may not in all respects be properly attributed to radiation. Williams (1957) has shown how the arbitrary activities of energetic taxonomists can create a spurious suggestion of diversity in just those horizons that they have studied. Such exaggerations may vitiate the quantitative comparison of one radiation with another, but they do not lesson the evidence that radiation has occurred. But even though cladogenesis can be inferred from such observations, it remains true that in the Ostracoda no evidence has been drawn from the consideration of speciation as such. Nor can cladogenesis within the species be easily detected in other groups of fossils.

There is a need in taxonomic theory for more rigorous palaeontological research into the origin of 'natural' taxonomic discontinuities. Most of the evidence supporting the theory of cladogenesis is drawn from neontology—from ecology, animal distribution, population genetics, and experimental taxonomy. Is there any fossil evidence at all for this process? The fossil record of the Quaternary vertebrates, and especially of mammals, strongly supports the polytypic species concept (see, for example, the summary given by Matthews (1952) of the British voles), and actual examples of cladogenesis leading to full speciation can be postulated from such evidence with a satisfactory degree of probability. But similar evidence is difficult to obtain from farther back in the fossil record, and seems a great deal more scanty among the invertebrates.

There are reasons for these difficulties, but when the reasons are understood, the difficulties should not prove insurmountable. If cladogenesis is to be detected, then its various phases should follow each other in successive horizons, but the taxonomic differentiates within each phase are only to be distinguished geographically. The distribution of a species in phase 1 will be wide, and perhaps spread over more than one continent or ocean. But it is always, in geological terms, very short-lived. In phase 2, geographical subspeciation or even speciation should occur, but once more this can only be detected over a wide geographical area. However, phases 2 and 3 are likely to be spread over a longer geological time, and it will not be necessary to demonstrate that the various geographical races are exactly contemporary. The real problem centres on the limitations imposed by the stratigraphical evidence available to the geologist. The geological record of a specific period in the past is incomplete because:

(i) it can only be preserved in those geographical areas in which deposition was taking place;
(ii) much of the deposit laid down at that time will since have been removed by erosion;
(iii) of the deposit left, the only part available to the geologist for examination will be that part exposed along a sinuous linear outcrop, or that part plumbed by relatively minute boreholes.

With these three limitations, the geologist has left for his examination but a tiny fraction of the surface of the earth as it existed at the time in question. He will indeed be fortunate if this fraction provides an adequate sample for deducing the previous geographical distribution of an animal species. Nevertheless some work of this nature has been achieved (e.g. Ager, 1956); but the palaeontological investigation of cladogenesis must inevitably be limited to species that are abundantly fossilized, and although the examination of the commonest fossils is not a pastime that will commend itself to all workers, it does seem probable that such studies will be as important to the general theory of evolution as will the more usual descriptive studies of rarities.

Acknowledgements. I am indebted to the helpful comments of Dr. A. J. Cain, Dr. T. D. Ford, and Dr. D. Nichols, who were kind enough to read through the first draft of the manuscript.

References

Ager, D. V., 1956. The geographical distribution of brachiopods in the British Middle Lias. *Quart. J. Geol. Soc.*, **112**, 157–87.

Bader, R. S., 1958. Similarity and recency in common ancestry. *Syst. Zool.*, **7**, 184–7.

Bigelow, R. S., 1958. Classification and phylogeny. Ibid., **7**, 49–59.
——— 1959. Similarity, ancestry and scientific principles. Ibid., **8**, 165–8.

Cain, A. J., 1958. Logic and memory in Linnaeus's system of taxonomy. *Proc. Linn. Soc. Lond.*, **169**, 144–63.

——— 1959. Deductive and inductive methods in post-Linnaean taxonomy. Ibid., **170**, 185–217.

——— and Harrison, G. A., 1958. An analysis of the taxonomist's judgement of affinity. *Proc. Zool. Soc. Lond.*, **131**, 85–98.

——— ——— 1960. Phyletic Weighting. Ibid., **135**, 1–31.

Chernysheva, N. E., 1960 (ed.). *Osnovÿ paleontologii.* Chlenictonogie trilobitoobraznye i rakoobraznye. Moscow, 515 pp.

Cox, L. R., 1960. Thoughts on the classification of the Gastropoda. *Proc. Malacol. Soc. Lond.*, **33**, 239–61.

Huxley, J. S., 1959. Clades and grades. *Syst. Assoc. Publ.*, **3**, 21–22.

Kiriakoff, S. G., 1959. Phylogenetic systematics versus typology. *Syst. Zool.*, **8**, 117–18.

Kollmann, K., 1960. Ostracoden aus der alpinen Trias Österreichs. I. *Parabairdia* n.g. und *Ptychobairdia* n.g. (*Bairdiidae*). *Jb. Geol. B.A.*, **5**, 79–105.

Matthews, L. H., 1952. *British Mammals.* 'The New Naturalist', London: Collins. 410 pp., 64 pls.

Moore, R. C., 1961 (ed.). *Treatise on Invertebrate Paleontology.* Part Q, Arthropoda 3 (Ostracoda). Univ. Kansas Press.

Müller, G. W., 1894. Die Ostracoden des Golfes von Neapel und der angrenzenden Meeresabschnitte. *Fauna und Flora des Golfes von Neapel,* Mon. 21, 412 pp., 404 pls.

Myers, G. S., 1960. Some reflections on phylogenetic and typological taxonomy. *Syst. Zool.,* **9,** 37–41.

Popper, K. R., 1959. *The Logic of Scientific Discovery.* London: Hutchinson, 450 pp.

Rensch, B., 1959. *Evolution Above the Species Level,* London: Methuen, 419 pp.

Reyment, R., and Reyment, E., 1959. *Bairdia îlaroensis* sp. nov. aus dem Paleozän Nigeriens und due Gültigkeit der Gattung *Bairdoppilata* (Ostr. Crust.). *Stockholm Contr. Geol.,* **3,** 59–68, pl. 1.

Sars, G. O., 1888. Nye Bidrag till Kundskaben om Middlehavets Invertebratfauna. 4. Ostracoda Mediterranea. *Arch. Math. Nat., Oslo,* **12,** 173–324, pls. 1–20.

——— 1922–8. *An Account of the Crustacea of Norway,* vol. 9, *Ostracoda,* Oslo (Bergen Mus.), 277 pp., 119 pls.

Scott, H. W., 1960. The classification of fossil Ostracoda. *Internat. Geol. Cong., Rep. 21 Sess. Norden,* Vol. Abst., pp. 54–55.

Simpson, G. G., 1961. *Principles of Animal Taxonomy.* Columbia Univ. Press, 247 pp.

Sylvester-Bradley, P. C., 1950. The shell of the ostracod genus *Bairdia. Ann. Mag. Nat. Hist.,* (12) **3,** 751–6.

——— 1960. *Geology and the History of Life.* Leicester Univ. Press, 27 pp.

Weller, J. M., 1949. Paleontologic classification. *J. Paleont.,* **23,** 680–90.

Williams, A., 1957. Evolutionary rates of brachiopods. *Geol. Mag.,* **94,** 201–11.

Wright, C. W., 1950. Paleontologic classification. *J. Paleont.,* **24,** 746–8.

Trends in Avian Systematics

Ernst Mayr

Population Systematics

The approach in classical systematics is almost, one might say, "administrative". Its question is: "What name shall I give this specimen?" Or, because in birds the determination of species is easy and routine: "To what subspecies does this bird belong?" This approach silently and erroneously assumes that subspecies are as objectively definable as species, and that species are composed of uniform sub-units, the subspe-

Reprinted by permission of the author and publisher from *The Ibis, 101:* 293–302, 1959.

cies. The difficulties of the subspecies were intensified by persistent attempts to consider the subspecies not merely as a practical device of the taxonomist but also as a "unit" of evolution. It was inevitable that sooner or later these misconceptions and misapplications of the subspecies concept would be seriously critized. This has been done by Whistler, Lack, Voous and other ornithologists as well as by the entomologists Wilson and Brown (1953). They point out that four features of geographic variation make it difficult to delimit subspecies objectively: (1) The tendency of different characters to show independent trends of geographic variation; (2) the independent re-occurrence of similar or taxonomically indistinguishable populations in widely separated areas ("polytopic subspecies"); (3) the occurrence of micro-geographic races within formally recognized subspecies; and (4) the arbitrariness of the degree of distinction selected by different authors as justifying subspecific separation of slightly differentiated local populations. These four phenomena reveal that it is impossible, in principle, to define subspecies non-arbitrarily. Furthermore they prove that the subspecies, as such, is not a unit of evolution and that it conceals much of the inter and intra-population variability of species. Yet it is this very oversimplification that makes the subspecies such a useful tool for the classifier, and accounts for the reluctance of the practising taxonomist to give up so useful a pigeon-holing device.

No matter how useful, indeed indispensable (Mayr, 1954), the subspecies terminology is, it is unsuitable for describing the population structure of species. The biologist who wants to analyze and understand the population structure of species can do this without reference to what one might call the curatorial category, the subspecies. For such a biologist, the local population, the *deme* (in the restricted sense), is the unit, and every subspecies is normally composed of many such demes.

When species are studied strictly from the viewpoint of population structure, it is found that they can be described in terms of three major population phenomena:

1. *The geographical isolate.* This term designates all geographically isolated populations, which have limited or no gene exchange with the other populations of the species. Any insular population is normally such an isolate and isolates are therefore particularly common near the periphery of the species range. Isolates are frequently of subspecies rank; sometimes they have not yet achieved the degree of taxonomic difference justifying subspecies rank; and finally, if the isolate is large enough, it may include more than one subspecies. The particular biological importance of the geographical isolate is that every isolate, regardless of its taxonomic rank, is an incipient species; it is an important unit of evolution.

2. *The population continuum.* The second element in the structure of

species is the continuous series of contiguous populations which make up the main body of the species. Even where, owing to the unsuitability of the habitat, there is an occasional minor break, such a break is bridged by steady dispersal, resulting in gene exchange among populations. For the taxonomist such a population continuum is characterized by clinal variation. Extreme populations in a continuum may be very different phenotypically and may justify subspecific recognition. However, more progressive workers realize that chopping up such continuous series of populations into numerous subspecies, widely overlapping in characters, is ill advised and conceals the actual biological facts.

3. *The zone of secondary intergradation.* Whenever a geographical isolate re-establishes contact with the main body of the species, it will interbreed with it, provided that the isolate has not yet attained full species rank. Depending on the degree of genetic and phenotypic difference achieved by the phenotypically isolated populations, a more or less distinct hybrid belt or zone of secondary intergradation will develop. The hybrid belt between the Carrion Crow *Corvus corone* and the Hooded Crow *C. cornix* is a particularly striking example, but similar usually less distinct fusion lines can be found in many species.

The population structure of any species of birds can be described in terms of these three elements. To make such an analysis of all species of a family, and to record the relative frequency of the three elements, is one of the steps leading to "comparative systematics" (Mayr, 1951). By assigning each isolate the potential of an incipient species, one can easily express in quantitative terms in what families of birds and in what geographic areas conditions are most favourable for speciation. It is sometimes claimed that geographical speciation takes place only on islands. My student, Dr. Allen Keast of the Australian Museum of Sydney, has analyzed the population structure of many species of Australian birds at my suggestion and found that there are enough geographic isolates on the mainland of Australia to allow for abundant speciation.

Recording the position of belts of secondary hybridization likewise reveals important information. It permits the reconstruction of formerly existing barriers and of the location of former "refuges" caused by drought conditions (as in Australia), or by glaciation (as in Eurasia and North America). His studies enabled Keast to reconstruct much of the recent faunal history of Australia. A similar analysis of the North American and Eurasian avifauna is urgently needed to determine the period and location of the separation and nature of the barriers. The barriers in the Pleistocene presumably consisted less in the ice itself than in the vegetational changes preceding and accompanying glaciation.

The population structure of a species may be examined not only from the historical-geographical viewpoint, but also from the environmental one. You are all familiar with the climatic rules such as Bergmann's Rule,

Allen's Rule and Gloger's Rule which describe regularities in the geographic variation of the species of warm-blooded vertebrates as conditioned by certain factors of the physical environment. For instance, mean body-size tends to increase towards the colder part of the species range, while the relative size of all extremities and appendages tends to decrease. It is now realized that these statistical laws—better called "Rules", because they are not all-or-none laws—show many exceptions. The phenotype is always a compromise between selection pressures and not infrequently environmental constellations overrule the particular selection pressure which would normally result in compliance with the climatic rules (Mayr, 1956). Snow (1954), for instance, has shown that in certain titmice there is a regular decrease in the relative size of the bill toward the cooler part of the range of the species until at a given latitude it has reached a minimum size. Apparently the bill cannot drop below a certain size and still remain a useful instrument. It will be one of the tasks of the coming years to examine each exception to these climatic rules and try to find the particular selective factor which is responsible for it. Snow discovered that in several species of Palearctic birds size maxima are reached in the mountains of the semi-arid subtropical belt (Atlas Mts., Iran). He ascribed this to the relatively long winter-day. Terrell Hamilton (1959) has found the same phenomenon in many species of North American birds which reach maximum size in northern Mexico and the adjacent parts of the southwestern United States rather than in the Arctic or sub-Arctic portions of their range, as one should expect from Bergmann's rule. The areas where maximum size is achieved are areas of considerable aridity, and Hamilton believes that not day-length, but a selective advantage in water conservation is responsible for this size increase at higher altitudes in arid areas (reduction of the respiratory surfaces). Other exceptions to Bergmann's rule are caused by migration, as demonstrated convincingly by Salomonsen (1955). Yet, as I implied earlier, the systematic study of the adaptive features of local bird populations has only begun. Cain (1955) has demonstrated that even some rather elusive aspects of colouration in parrots and pigeons can be correlated with specific aspects of local climate or biotic environment.

It will be evident to you by now why the study of the population structure of species is an area of such great concern in the new systematics of birds. It permits determination of the past and present environmental factors responsible for the distribution of populations and for their phenotypes. It endeavors to supplement descriptive systematics with causal systematics.

Phylogenetic Systematics

The second major area of the—if I may use the phrase—newest systematics of birds, is actually the revival of an old field with the help of new methods and revised concepts. It is the study of the relationship of the species and genera of birds and their classification into higher categories, that is, into families and orders. Considering how little progress in bird classification has been made during the last 70 years (since Fürbringer 1888), the need for revival is obvious. The time has come for a renewed study of the higher categories of birds, now that the description of new species and subspecies is no longer the green pasture it was during the preceding two generations. Classification is essentially a two-step procedure. The first step, the discrimination of the basic units, the species, is remarkably far advanced in ornithology. This step, which causes so much trouble for the paleontologist and the student of microorganisms, is no problem for the ornithologist. There are hardly any cases left where it can be argued whether two forms are individual variants or species, or whether a "species" is really a complex of sibling species. It is with the second step of classification, the arrangement of species into genera, families, orders and super-orders, that so little progress has been made in 70 years. Indeed, as correctly emphasized by Stresemann, we seem to be further than ever away from a sound system. Even some of the characters accepted as reliable by Fürbringer in his great system of birds, have turned out to be unreliable. This is true for the leg structure of diving birds, *Podiceps, Gavia, Hesperornis* (Stolpe, 1932), the structure of the palate (Hofer, 1955), and the tarsal scutellation (Blaszyk, 1935).

Many of the taxonomic characters discovered since Fürbringer have likewise turned out to be unreliable, for instance, the frontal lacrimal region in the skull of plovers (Bock, 1958, *versus* Lowe, 1922), the jaw muscles of passeres (Mayr, 1955, *versus* Beecher, 1953), and the "palatomaxillaries" of passeres (Bock MS. *versus* Tordoff, 1954).

There are a number of reasons why it is so much more difficult to reconstruct the phylogeny of birds than that of mammals or reptiles. The first is that the fossil record has been so disappointing. The major radiation of birds seems to have taken place in the Cretaceous, more than 75 million years ago. Yet we have virtually no avian fossils from that period. Tertiary fossils belong clearly either to modern lines or to extinct side-branches. Indeed, I think it is fair to state that, with the spectacular exception of *Archaeopteryx*, there is not a single case in which a fossil bird has helped us to improve our classification.

There is a second reason for the difficulties of the avian macrotaxonomist. The invasion of the new evolutionary niche, the air, has given birds an enormous advantage, permitting wider dispersal into climatic zones, remote islands and a great diversity of habitats, than found in any other terrestrial vertebrate. As a consequence speciation has been rampant. The 8600 known species of birds compare, for instance, with an estimated number of only 3500 species of mammals. Yet, this very air-niche has also severely limited the evolutionary potential of birds. Birds can make evolutionary experiments with peripheral characters, characters that adapt to specific habitat- and food-niches, but any more drastic reconstruction might lower the efficiency of the flying machine. As a consequence, all birds are basically rather similar to each other. This claim does not preclude numerous differences among the families and orders of birds, but most of these differences are of limited use to the student of phylogeny, since they are *ad hoc* answers to very specific functional needs. The common possession of a cone-shaped bill does not make all of the seed-eating passeres a natural family. And the "taxonomic characters" that were formerly used to combine "shrikes" or "flycatchers" or "titmice," have turned out to be polyphyletic adaptations to specific food-niches, and each of these groups is now separated into several families or subfamilies. That such a polyphyletic origin might be true even for the Accipitres, as stated by several recent bird anatomists and reconfirmed by Starck cannot be ruled out. Considering the extreme similarity of hawks and falcons it is a disconcerting thought that they might not be closely related.

Are all the attempts to reconstruct the avian phylogeny perhaps hopeless? To draw that conclusion would seem to me prematurely pessimistic. There are two developments, in particular, that give us new hope, and that may permit the development of a new systematics of the higher categories.

A Revision of the Concepts of Phylogeny

The study of phylogeny has been dominated until quite recently by various pre-Darwinian metaphysical concepts. According to these, all evolution goes from lower to higher, forever pushing in the direction of perfection. "Simple" then means primitive or ancestral.

We now know that complexity of a structure is not necessarily an indication of evolutionary progress. Cases of secondary simplification are sufficiently frequent to make quite inadmissable the assumption that morphological series from simple to complex are necessarily evolutionary series. Without fossil evidence it is usually difficult to determine what is "primitive" and what "advanced."

A second important change in our concepts concerns the evolution of a "type" (in the morphological, not the nomenclatural meaning of the word). It used to be assumed that a type shows an equal rate of evolution for all of its structures. If it was advanced for one character, it would have to be advanced also for the others. This archetypal thinking about evolution has misled evolutionists again and again. We now know that every part of an organism evolves at its own rate. In the case of *Archaeopteryx* the feathers were the only structure already 100% avian while every other structure was still to a greater or lesser extent reptilian. This is mosaic evolution as described by Sir Gavin de Beer (1954) for

Archaeopteryx but long known to paleontologists. We shall see when we discuss the weighting of characters how important the understanding of mosaic evolution is in the classification of birds.

Taxonomic Characters

The relative merits of different types of characters have been argued in taxonomy almost from the very beginning. In birds particularly, with their extraordinary basic similarity, an entire classification may depend on the weight given to a single diagnostic character. In the earlier classifications, structural differences of the bill, the feet, and the feathers were given foremost weight. Before 1800, however, certain features of the internal anatomy were already increasingly utilized. Equally early, there was occasional reference to the importance of behavioural characters. No less a biologist than Alfred R. Wallace emphasized the importance of behaviour as an aid to taxonomy, in an early volume of *The Ibis* (1864:36–41). Wallace believed with Owen "that those parts of an animal which have the least immediate connection with its habits and economy (= ecology) are exactly those which best exhibit deep-seated and obscure affinities. The wings, the feet and the beak in birds may undergo the most extraordinary modifications in the same group in accordance with differences of habit and of external conditions, while at the same time, such apparently insignificant characters as the general colouring, the texture of the plumage, the scaling of the tarsi, and the colour and texture of the eggs remain constant, and reveal the true relations of the species." Seebohm (1881:viii) likewise came to the conclusion that the so-called structural characters of bill, feet and wings are of only minor importance. "It has been accepted as an axiom among ornithologists that genera must be founded upon structural characters." He continues that the longer he worked with them, the less he relied on these characters, until finally: "I have convinced myself that these so-called structural characters have no generic value at all, and I have been obliged to fall back upon colour, or pattern of colour as the only character which indicates near relationship. In my opinion the pattern of the colour in the family of Turdinae is a character which is more trustworthy (as showing community of origin), which in fact dates further back than the shape of the wings, tail or bill." In these views, expressed also in his monograph of the Charadrii (1888) Seebohm was in his time distinctly in the minority, if not alone. It is only within the last few decades that we have fully realized how plastic in birds the bill is, and the shape of the wing, and how extraordinarily conservative often the colour pattern.

Yet even the combination of morphology and colour pattern may be insufficient to permit a decision in difficult situations. There has been a constant search for new characters, indeed, for characters of a novel type. I have recently summarized some of my views on the use of behaviour in classification (Mayr, 1958a) and since Dr. Tinbergen will discuss this topic in today's session, I will say no more about it.

One after another novel type of taxonomic clue is discovered, only to disappoint us subsequently. The parasites are a case in point. Parasites evolve together with their hosts and, being often more conservative and less apt to enter specialized ecological niches than their hosts, they might provide clues where functional adaptations have obliterated the phylogenetic trail. Clay (1951, 1957) has suggested many fascinating possibilities as to revisions of the accepted avian classification, on the basis of host distribution of genera of Mallophaga. Yet one must be cautious. Mallophaga seem to transfer to a new host more readily than is usually realized (Mayr, 1957) and similarity of the plumage may facilitate such a transfer. If tropic birds (*Phaethon*) have Mallophaga clearly related to those of terns (Laridae) it does not mean that they are related to the terns, but merely that they were invaded by a group of bird lice normally found on terns. The fact that the same three genera of bird lice occur on flamingoes and ducks indicates that there has been a colonization from one host to another. If flamingoes and ducks had originated from a common root, one would expect related but different genera in the two groups. The fact that the distribution of the cestodes, as host-specific as the bird lice, fails to correlate with the distributional pattern of the bird lice in nearly all of the crucial cases (Baer, 1957), weakens still further our confidence in the infallibility of parasites as clues to the relationship of their hosts. This does not mean that bird lice are altogether useless as taxonomic indicators, but it does mean that one cannot rely on them blindly.

Chemical methods have been utilized in recent years to an increasing extent, particularly various methods based on protein differences. The earliest of these is the serological method of the precipitation reaction. This method, unfortunately, is not very sensitive and often yields ambiguous results. Although Boyden and his school have been working with this method for more than 30 years, I am not aware of any improvement in avian taxonomy as a result of the work. Three additional methods have been tried in recent years. One is analysis of blood-group genes, applied by Irwin (1947) in the study of the relationships of certain species of *Columba* and *Streptopelia*, and by Mainardi (1957) to determine the relationships of certain genera of finches. A second method is that of paper chromatography, which I applied for several years to a considerable number of species of birds without ever publishing my results because they were not fully consistent. More recently Mainardi (1958) has also utilized this method in a study of the relationships of gallinaceous genera. The results so far confirm the accepted classification.

The latest technique is that of the electrophoresis of egg-white proteins. It was introduced into ornithology by McCabe and Deutsch (1952) who showed that the method was indeed a useful test of relationship.

They found considerable similarity between *Aythya* and *Anas* in the distribution of the egg-white proteins, confirming a relationship previously proposed by Delacour and Mayr (1945) on the basis of a study of the downy young and certain behaviour characters. Sibley (1958) has recently taken up this technique with a vastly improved apparatus and consequently increased accuracy. His work has already contributed considerably to our knowledge, although it indicates that even this technique may not be infallible. The egg-white profile of the turkey (*Meleagris*) "falls approximately intermediate between the Ring-necked Pheasant and the Domestic Fowl" which surely no one will consider to be its true phylogenetic position.

Useful as all these new techniques are, they cannot replace good, sound comparative anatomy. We are in the midst of the rediscovery of this strangely neglected field of ornithological research. One museum after the other has started to build up collections of skeletons and spirit specimens, and more and more of the younger ornithologists are turning from micro-taxonomy to macro-taxonomy. This development, which is to be welcomed with all possible praise, may require patience and tolerance on our part. Let us frankly admit it, the great tradition of comparative anatomy is dead. To enter this field, a young man cannot go to study with one of the great masters. Gegenbaur, Fürbringer and the others died more than a generation ago. The comparative anatomy of today is, in some respects, a brand new field, and will have to overcome certain childhood diseases (Mayr, 1955). And even those authors of recent publications in this field who succeeded in avoiding major mistakes in method or interpretation, have failed to make much contribution to an understanding of avian relationship: their papers are either too purely descriptive or too purely functional. But perhaps I am over-impatient; perhaps what we need is such a return to the primary basis. Indeed, no character can be utilized successfully in taxonomy that is not correctly described and whose function we have not at least tried to understand.

Systematics is based on the correct evaluation of "systematic characters," and we should pay far greater attention to an understanding of what we mean by "character." If a habit like that of eating seeds results in the simultaneous modification of the bill, the horny palate, the bony palate, the tongue, and the jaw muscles, it would be improper to count each of these individual structures as a separate character. Likewise, if two kinds of wing-divers, like a diving petrel and an auk, acquire similar proportions of body, wings and legs, it would be quite misleading—not to use a stronger word—to count each of these changed proportions as a separate character. It is the totality of proportions and structures of the extremities of these birds which combine in the single character complex of "wing-diving." A "character" in the evolutionary or phylogenetic sense is often a whole complex of structures. This has to be remembered in considering the problem of whether or not to "weight" characters.

There are at present two schools: those who want to give all characters equal weight (no doubt a reaction to the many ill-fated single-character classifications); and those who want to weight characters carefully, basing the weight on the amount of "information" conveyed by a character. In view of the results of following blindly conclusions based on piles of unweighted characters (which leads, for instance, Verheyen (1958) to place the diving petrels in the same order as the auks, and both near the penguins), I am strongly inclined towards a system of careful weighting. No electric computer has so far been able to surpass in the arrangement of higher categories, the integrating power of the brain of an intelligent and experienced taxonomist. And in the hands of our less gifted colleagues even the best computer would produce absurd systems.

With this comment we come to the purely practical question of the system of birds. Is there an answer to the simple question: "Which is the best system?" Or perhaps I should ask first: "Is there a 'best' system?" and: "How would we recognize it?" The first step in making a system is the analytical delineation of the basic entities, the genera, the subfamilies, the families; and the second step is the grouping together of those which we consider to be related. It may not sound like new systematics if I ask such simple questions as, are the kinglets *Regulus* more closely related to the warblers *Phylloscopus* or to the titmice *Parus;* are the nearest relatives of the water-ouzels *Cinclus* the thrushes (Turdidae), or the wrens (Troglodytidae); are the woodpeckers (Pici) the nearest relatives of the Passeres, or of the hummingbirds (Trochili); are the falcons (Falconidae) more closely related to the Accipitridae, or as Starck (1959) has suggested, to the owls (Strigidae)? These questions may be old systematics, but answers can come only from the newest systematics. And the answer, in all cases where we can find an answer, leads to interesting biological questions.

What is the probability that we will find answers to all these questions and to the hundreds of additional ones the avian taxonomist would like to ask? Stresemann (1959) has recently surveyed this field and has expressed optimism, as far as relationships within the orders are concerned, but pessimism as to whether it will ever be possible to join together the major orders of birds. Indeed the outlook is not promising, considering the great age of these subdivisions, and considering the functional plasticity of birds.

Even less promising are the widespread endeavours to find a "best" sequence of the orders and families of birds. The impossibility of finding objective criteria to determine what is "high" and what "low," what "primitive" and what secondarily simplified, makes it quite evident that such endeavours are rather futile. The fact that all phyletic evolution is "mosaic" evolution makes our task even more hopeless. Shall we rate the penguins, the hummingbirds, or the songbirds as most advanced? All three have reached an evolutionary pinnacle, but each group with a different set of properties.

I have lately (Mayr, 1958b) called attention to the fact that mosaic evolution is dominant among the passerine birds. One group, while remaining conservative with respect to the structure of bill and feet, may be highly progressive with respect to the central nervous system or social behaviour patterns. Other groups, like the finches or various families of nectar-feeding birds, may become highly specialized with respect to bill, tongue, palate and accessory organs, yet remain conservative with respect to most other characters. Such a state of affairs poses a virtually unsurmountable problem. Our taxonomic system is a linear sequence of families. We start with those we call the most primitive or "lowest," and end with those we consider most progressive or "highest." It would be possible to arrange the families in such a sequence if all characters progressed at an even rate and if every family could be placed easily somewhere along this progression. But what shall we do when one family is primitive in characters 1, 2 and 3 and highly advanced in 4, while another family is very primitive in characters 2, 3 and 4, and highly advanced for character 1? It simply boils down to a value judgment as to the relative importance of characters 1, 2, 3, and 4. When Seebohm (1881) wrote the introduction to the thrush volume of the *Catalogue of Birds* he stated: "the species included in this volume are admitted by most modern ornithologists to be the most highly developed group of birds. Amongst them are found the finest songsters, showing the highest development of the vocal organs, whilst few families can rival them in their powers of flight." Other authors have equally emphatically singled out the Corvidae as the "highest" group of birds owing to the high development of the central nervous system found in this family. Still others consider the extraordinary courtship habits of the birds of paradise and bower birds as deserving top ranking. In his classification of birds Wetmore (1951) writes: "I have placed the Fringillidae at the end of the list, because of my feeling that this group is the modern expression of a main core or stem that through the earlier Tertiary periods has given rise to more specialized assemblages that we now recognize as distinct families."

All these are legitimate choices, but what criterion is there to permit an objective decision? Special feeders, like seed-eaters and nectar-feeders, are among the most aberrant oscines, morphologically. Are they "high" or merely a "dead-end" side-branch? The versatility demanded from the omnivorous forms, like the Corvidae and some starlings, has placed a high selective premium on the development of the higher brain-centers in these families. Is this going to be good or bad for their futures? In view of the complete absence of objective criteria I consider it wisest to follow the sequence proposed by the Committee appointed at the Basel Congress.

Conclusion

It may have appeared to you that I have deviated far from my assigned topic. Yet I feel that we must have a clear understanding of the problems of avian systematics before we can chart the course of the new systematics. I think this course is now clearly evident. On one hand the avian systematist will occupy himself with the population structure of species and will determine the historical events responsible for the pattern of distribution and the environmental factors responsible for the geographic variation of the characters. On the other hand he will concentrate on the higher categories. He will utilize new sources of information provided by previously unused characters of behaviour and physiology to determine relationships between genera, families and orders. He will make a new try at comparative anatomy, but perhaps a more sophisticated comparative anatomy than that of our classical authors. And he will evaluate all these characters and character complexes in the light of the new concepts of evolution.

Let us hope that this new systematics will be as stimulating and productive as was the no longer so new systematics of the last 25 years.

References

Baer, J. G. 1957. Répartition et endémicité des Cestodes chez les Reptiles, Oiseaux et Mammi fères. First Symposium on host specificity among parasites of Vertebrates, Neuchâtel 1957 : 270–292. Inst. Zool. Univ. Neuchâtel.

Beecher, W. J. 1953. A phylogeny of the oscines. Auk 70 : 270–333.

de Beer, G. 1954. Archaeopteryx lithographica. Brit. Mus. (Nat. Hist.) London.

Blaszyk, P. 1935. Untersuchungen über die Stammesgeschichte der Vogelschuppen und Federn und über Abhängigkeit ihrer Ausbildung am Vogelfuss von der Funktion. Gegenbaurs Morph. Jahrb., Leipzig 75 : 483–521, 522–567.

Bock, W. J. 1958. A generic review of the plovers (Charadriidae, Aves). Bull. Mus. Comp. Zool. 118 (2) : 27–97.

Bock, W. J. MS. The palatine process of the premaxilla in the passeres.

Cain, A. J. 1954. Animal Species and their Evolution. London.

Cain, A. J. 1955. A revision of *Trichoglossus haematodus* and of the Australian platycercine parrots. Ibis 97 : 432–479.

Clay, T. 1951. The Mallophaga as an aid to the classification of birds with special reference to the structure of feathers. Proc. 10. Int. Orn. Congr. Uppsala : 207–215.

Clay, T. 1957. The Mallophaga of birds. First symposium on host specificity among parasites of Vertebrates, Neuchâtel, 1957 : 120–158. Inst. Zool. Univ. Neuchâtel.

Delacour, J. & Mayr, E. 1945. The family Anatidae. Wilson Bull. 57 : 1–55.

Fürbringer, M. 1888. Untersuchungen zur Morphologie und Systematik der Vōgel. Jena.

Hamilton, T. H. 1959. Adaptive variation in the genus *Vireo.* Wilson Bull. 70 : 307–346.

Hofer, H. 1955. Neuere Untersuchungen zur Kopfmorphologie der Vōgel. Acta 11 Congr. Int. Orn. Basel 1954 : 104–137.

Huxley, J. (edit.). 1940. The New Systematics. Oxford.

Irwin, M. R. 1947. Immunogenetics. Advances in Genetics 1 : 133–159.

Lowe, P. R. 1922. On the significance of certain characters in some charadriine genera, with a provisional classification of the order Charadriiformes. Ibis 62 : 475–495.

Mainardi, D. 1957. Affinitá sierologiche e filogenesi nei Fringillidi. Arch. Zool. Ital. 42 : 151–159.

Mainardi, D. 1958. La filogenesi nei fringillidi basata sui rapporti immunologici. Rendiconti, 1st. Lombardo–Accad. Sci. Lett., Milano. Sci. (B) 92 : 336–356.

Mayr, E. 1942. Systematics and the Origin of Species. New York.

Mayr, E. 1951. Speciation in birds. Proc. 10 Int. Orn. Congr. Uppsala 1951 : 91–131.

Mayr, E. 1954. Notes on nomenclature and classification. Syst. Zool. 3 : 86–89.

Mayr, E. 1955. Comments on some recent studies of song bird phylogeny. Wilson Bull. 67 : 33–44.

Mayr, E. 1956. Geographical character gradients and climatic adaptation. Evolution 10 : 105–108.

Mayr, E. 1957. Evolutionary aspects of host specificity among parasites of vertebrates. First Symposium on host specificity among parasites of Vertebrates, Neuchâtel, 1957 : 7–14, 169–170. Inst. Zool. Univ. Neuchâtel.

Mayr, E. 1958a. Behaviour and systematics, *in* Behaviour and Evolution, Anne Roe and G. G. Simpson, editors, Yale Univ. Press, New Haven.

Mayr, E. 1958b. The sequence of the songbird families. Condor 60 : 194–195.

Mayr, E., Linsley, E. G. & Usinger, R. L. 1953. Methods and Principles of systematic Zoology. New York.

McCabe, R. A. & Deutsch, H. F. 1952. The relationships of certain birds as indicated by their egg white proteins. Auk 69 : 1–18.

Rensch, B. 1947. Neuere Probleme der Abstammungslehre. Stuttgart.

Salomonsen, F. 1955. The evolutionary significance of bird-migration. Dansk. Biol. Medd. 22(6) : 1–62.

Seebohm, H. 1881. Catalogue of birds. V. Turdidae. Brit. Mus. (Nat. Hist.), London.

Seebohm, H. 1888. The geographical distribution of the family Charadriidae. London.

Sibley, C. G. 1958. The electrophoretic patterns of egg-white proteins as taxonomic characters. Mimeo.

Snow, D. W. 1954. Trends in geographical variation in Palearctic members of the genus *Parus*. Evolution 8 : 19–28.

Starck, D. 1959. Neuere Ergebnisse der vergleichenden Anatomie, erläutert an der Trigeminus Muskulatur der Vögel. J. Orn. 100 : 47–59.

Stolpe, M. 1932. Physiologisch-anatomische Untersuchungen über die hintere Extremität der Vögel. J. Orn. 80 : 161–247.

Stresemann, E. 1951. Die Entwicklung der Ornithologie. Berlin.

Stresemann, E. 1959. The current status of avian classification. Auk *in press.* Tordoff, H. B. 1954. A systematic study of the avian family Fringillidae based on the structure of the skull. Misc. Publ. Mus. Zool. Univ. Michigan 81 : 1–41.

Verheyen, R. 1958. Contribution à la systematique des Alciformes. Inst. Roy. Sci. Nat. Belgique 34(45) : 1–15.

Wetmore, A. 1951. A revised classification for the birds of the world. Smithson. Misc. Coll. 117(4) : 1–22.

Wilson, E. O. & Brown, W. L. Jr. 1953. The subspecies concept and its taxonomic application. Systematic Zoology 2 : 97–111.

3 / Genecology and Evolution

During the last two decades evolutionary studies have been focused upon problems of microevolution—the genecology, or biosystematics, of the relatively small changes that lead to the genetical separation of populations and to incipient speciation. This period has seen extensive work on plant ecotypes, beginning with the classical studies of the Swedish genecologist Turesson and continuing with such careful and detailed investigations as those of Gregor in Scotland. The paper by the American worker C. McMillan emphasizes the fact that genecological behavior cannot be separated from its ecological implications.

At the same time, evolutionary studies have passed from the observational, and even anecdotal, phase of Darwinism to the enunciation of experimentally determinable hypotheses. A paper by the distinguished geneticist G. Ledyard Stebbins, who enjoys an international reputation as an investigator of the causes of variation in plants, ably presents this new genetical approach. Other aspects of genetics are described in another book in this present series—*Gene Theory* by Elof A. Carlson.

Some conflicts arising from the increasing application of the theory of natural selection to ecological and evolutionary aspects of environmental problems—are discussed in the paper by G. H. Orians.

Ecotypes and Community Function

Calvin McMillan

Introduction

Three statements can be given concerning the ecotype and community function. The first: "The role of the ecotype in community function is primarily one of allowing vegetation to adjust to its habitat." The second: "The simultaneous selection of ecotypic variants within different kinds of plants occupying a common area results in the harmony of a particular stand of vegetation, the community, and its habitat." The third: "The selection of eco-genetic gradients within a number of species results in the continuity of a kind of vegetation, the community-type, over habitat diversity."

Within these three introductory statements, ecotype, ecotypic variation, and eco-genetic gradient refer to genetically-determined variation that is habitat-correlated. Following sampling in habitat extremes genetic

Reprinted by permission of the author and publisher from *The American Naturalist, 94:* 246–55, 1960.

differences are usually recognized: edaphic ecotypes, climatic ecotypes, topographic ecotypes, etc. A pattern of ecotypic variation often emerges from sampling in habitats of varying degrees of difference. An eco-genetic gradient often results from sampling through a habitat gradient. Variation observed in the field and possibly habitat-correlated is ecodemal until experimentally substantiated (Gregor, 1944, 1946).

In these statements, the concept *community* is applied to one or more populations in a common spatial arrangement, and the concept *population* is applied to the one or more individuals of a close genetic lineage in a common spatial arrangement. Therefore, there are many kinds of communities, as there are many kinds of populations. The lumping or sorting of certain communities into a particular kind, on any of a number of criteria, results in the recognition of a community-type. Mainly under discussion will be the community-type based on the geographic repetition of a certain combination of species and genera.

In the following discussion, an evaluation of the evidence supporting each statement will be presented. The validity of the first statement concerning the role of the ecotype in community function lies in the demonstration of ecotypic variation and of its correlation with the conditions of the habitat. The second statement concerning the simultaneous selection of ecotypic variants within different kinds of organisms in a given area applies to the harmony between a local community and its habitat. The investigation of the genetic potential of the various community members and the behavioral patterns under different site potentials would aid in this analysis. The uniqueness of a local community can be determined by a comparison with other communities of the same community-type. The third statement concerning the selection of eco-genetic gradients within a number of species is applied to the geographic repetition of a combination of certain species and genera. The analysis of ecotypic variation within a series of species critical to the recognition of such a community-type, and the comparative analysis of the members of a number of communities would support this statement.

Ecotypic Variation

Natural selection commonly results in a pattern of ecotypic variation within a plant species. In validation of the first statement is the general occurrence of ecotypes among trees (Pinus, Langlet, 1943; Stoeckeler and Rudolf, 1956; Kramer, 1957; Acer, Kriebel, 1957; Vaartaja, 1959; Thuja, Habeck, 1958; Vaartaja, 1959; Pseudotsuga, Morris, et al., 1957; Irgens-Moller, 1957; Tsuga, Olson, et al., 1959; Vaartaja, 1959; Fraxinus, Wright, 1944a, 1944b; Vaartaja, 1959; Meuli and Shirley, 1937; Betula, Larix, Picea, Ulmus, Vaartaja, 1959; Populus, Pauley and Perry, 1954), among shrubs (Artemisia, Ward, 1953; Clausen, et al., 1940; Atriplex, Turesson.

1922, 1925; current studies in Prosopis, McMillan, unpubl.), among grasses (Bouteloua, Olmsted, 1944; Riegal, 1940; McMillan, 1959; Andropogon, Larsen, 1947; Cornelius, 1947; McMillan, 1959, Poa, Hiesey, 1953a; Deschampsia, Lawrence, 1945; Panicum, Nielsen, 1944, 1947; McMillan and Weiler, 1959; McMillan, 1959; Sporobolus, Sorghastrum, Elymus, Koeleria, McMillan, 1959; Festuca, Bradshaw and Snaydon, 1959), among herbs (Achillea, Potentilla, Clausen, et al., 1940, 1948; Hiesey, 1953b; Viola, Clausen, 1922, 1926; Geranium, Bōcher, 1947; Plantago, Gregor, 1939; Solidago, Goodwin, 1944; Armeria, Baker, 1949, 1953; Helianthus, Heiser, 1954; Eupatorium, Kucera 1958; Streptanthus, Gilia, Kruckeberg, 1951), to cite a partial list. Among animal species, the demonstration of ecotypic variation is less general, but examples are found among insects (Drosophila, Dobzhansky, 1948; Lymantria, Goldschmidt, 1934; Colias, Hovanitz, 1945), among amphibians (Rana, Moore, 1944, 1947, 1949), among fishes (Gasterosteus, Heuts, 1947, 1949), and among rodents (Peromyscus, Dice, 1933).

The above examples have been empirically determined and correlated with the habitat. In many instances the genetics of the ecological races has been studied extensively and was the subject of a recent review by Clausen and Hiesey. The habitat correlations have been various: light period sequence, temperature period sequence, soil moisture, length of growing season, among others. In 15 species out of 17 in eight of nine tree genera (Acer, Betula, Fraxinus, Larix, Picea, Pinus, Pseudotsuga, and Ulmus), Vaartaja showed photoperiod ecotypes were correlated with the latitude of seed origin. These genera, in addition to Populus, in which Pauley and Perry demonstrated photoperiod ecotypes, represent the most widespread trees north of the tropics. In *Pseudotsuga taxifolia*, Morris, *et al.* (1957) found early bud-bursting by trees from localities having warm spring days and nights, as in wide valleys. Those with intermediate bursting buds came from higher elevations, with cold spring days and nights. Trees with latest bursting buds came from narrow valleys where cold air drainage resulted in warm spring days and cold spring nights. The characteristic bud bursting was maintained over a period of 22 years at three altitudinal plantations. Among 43 sources of *Acer saccharum*, Kriebel (1957) showed terminal dormancy was correlated with latitude. Stoeckeler and Rudolf (1956) showed growth patterns correlated with latitudinal origin among 29 sources of *Pinus banksiana*. Habeck (1958) demonstrated ecotypic differences in *Thuja occidentalis* in Wisconsin. Those from lowland swamps had growth patterns different from the upland type when grown in the same habitat. Goodwin showed a flowering gradient in *Solidago sempervirens*. Clones from Massachusetts flowered sooner in Rochester, New York, than those from Maryland or Florida. The later flowering of more southerly clones was correlated with the longer growing season toward the south. McMillan (1959) has demonstrated early maturing types from northerly latitudes and high altitudes in Bouteloua, Andropogon, Panicum, Sorghastrum, and Sporobolus. In seven species within these five grass genera, clones of later maturity were from areas with longer growing seasons. In Achillea, Hiesey (1953b) demonstrated that the race from the northern California coast was able to flower under cool day and night conditions. The race from the Great Valley of California flowered under high day and night temperatures. This flowering response under controlled temperatures was correlated with the temperatures of their native habitats during their usual flowering period. In species of several genera (Silene, Plantago, Armeria, etc.) the maritime populations have been later in flowering and more prostrate than the inland form. While this list includes only a few examples, it indicates the general occurrence of habitat-correlated variation in plants.

The general occurrence of ecotypic variation within plant species strongly supports the view that ecotypes play a significant role in vegetational adaptation. There have been few instances in which ecotypic variation has not been demonstrated within a widespread plant species. This could result from a hesitance to publish what is generally considered to be the normal. However, since ecotypic variation is becoming the expected mechanism for wide plant distribution, perhaps non-variable species will gain more attention. Of 11 grass species studied in Mid-America by McMillan (1957, 1959), only Stipa showed a lack of habitat-correlated variation. In three species, *Stipa spartea, S. comata,* and *S. leucotricha,* behavioral characteristics were very similar within a species for clones from widely separated and extremely different habitats. In local populations of Stipa, the observed differences within the species, result chiefly from the local habitat sequence in that particular year.

Community Adaptation

The evidence for evaluating the second statement, concerning community adaptation, and the third, concerning the continuity of a community-type, will be drawn largely from studies of the grasslands of Mid-America. This is necessitated by the scarcity of studies dealing with the role of the ecotype in community function, resulting, in part, from the emphasis of the taxonomist upon studies of ecotypic variation, and from the associated lack of emphasis by the ecologist. However, the original studies of Turesson (1922, 1925) in genecology are particularly note worthy owing to their ecological viewpoint. In these transplant studies, Turesson demonstrated characteristics common to many maritime ecotypes within a number of herbaceous species in Sweden. His comparison with ecotypes of the same species from inland habitats formed a sound basis for the ecological evaluation of communities. The later transplant studies of Clausen, Keck, and Hiesey (1940) dealt with herbaceous species from forested areas in California. Alpine ecotypes in a number of species were differentiated from sub-montane ecotypes and these in turn from foothill and coastal ecotypes. Their studies in Achillea (1948), involving more frequent sampling along an altitudinal gradient in the Sierra Nevada, suggest that eco-genetic gradients may exist in many of the species studied earlier.

An ecological objection to the studies of both Turesson and of Clausen, Keck, and Hiesey is that there was no evaluation of the ecological dominants, that is, the most conspicuous plants, trees, in a forested area. Although both give evidence of the simultaneous selection of ecotypes within a number of herbaceous species in a common habitat, ecologists have relegated these studies to taxonomy. Ecologists have considered alpine communities distinct from sub-alpine communities and these distinct from lower altitudinal communities, because of the different assemblages of ecological dominants involved. The occurrence of a gradient of ecotypes within herbaceous species does not alter the observed zonation of forest types in the Sierra Nevada.

The grassland vegetation offers a superb object of study for determining the relationship of ecotypes to community function. Here, the ecological dominants, the grasses, are well suited to an ecotypic analysis. Here, also, the combination of certain species and genera remains fairly constant over an obviously variable habitat. It was reasoned, therefore, that studies of ecotypic variation in grasslands might be focused effectively upon a better understanding of the community and of the distribution of a particular community-type. The earlier studies of workers in the Soil Conservation Service, agronomists, and other ecologists in demonstrating behavioral variation within the common grass species were instrumental in directing the future course of these studies. For example, the studies of Olmsted (1944) and his students presented evidence in *Bouteloua curtipendula* of ecotypes differing in response to length of light period, the northern forms flowering under longer light periods and the southern forms under shorter light periods. The studies of Cornelius (1947) and of Larsen (1947) in *Andropogon scoparius* demonstrated behavioral patterns attuned to shorter growing seasons by northern forms and to longer growing seasons by more southerly forms.

In the grassland investigations to be evaluated here, the focus has been upon (a) the behavior of individual plants, (b) the comparison of behavior patterns within a population, and (c) the comparison of behavior patterns in a number of populations within the same community. The studies have included an analysis of behavior patterns under natural habitat conditions as well as a number of experimental habitats including transplant gardens in Lincoln, Nebraska, and Austin, Texas, and controlled greenhouse conditions.

In six grass species in Nebraska, McMillan (1957) showed that populations from a southeastern community began flowering two weeks later than populations from a sandhill community of central Nebraska. Populations of both communities showed behavioral differences when compared in the loess soils at Lincoln and in the sandy soils near Halsey. When grown in the sandhills, all of the populations were approximately two weeks later in flowering than when grown 200 miles further east in Lincoln at a similar latitude. This basic study has been expanded to include grassland communities from southern Saskatchewan and Manitoba to southern Texas.

From a community in the vicinity of Watertown, South Dakota, clones of seven populations were studied in the transplant garden (McMillan, 1959): *Bouteloua gracilis, Bouteloua curtipendula, Andropogon scoparius, Panicum virgatum, Sporobolus heterolepis, Andropogon gerardi,* and *Sorghastrum nutans.* During 1958 at Lincoln, Nebraska, all of the clones flowered prior to July 18. From a community near Manhattan, Kansas, clones of populations representing the same seven species had initial flowering at Lincoln after July 18. Initial flowering in the Kansas clones extended into mid-September. In an eighth population (*Stipa spartea*) from South Dakota and from Kansas, similar behavior was shown. In a ninth population (*Elymus canadensis*), the earliest flowering was in the clones from the southernmost community. In reducing the communities to symbolic form, with the prime indicating early maturity, they could be represented as follows: Watertown, South Dakota, a, b, c′, d′, e′, f′, g′, h′, i′, and Manhattan, Kansas, a, b′, c, d, e, f, g, h, i. Each community is unique, though the same combination of species is represented. Each is in harmony with its habitat through the selection of ecotypic variants in eight of the nine species studied. Included within those nine species were those characterizing the true prairie type of community of Clements (1936), and representing five of the six community-types used by Weaver (1954) in his analysis of the true prairie.

The members of two communities, one at Fertile, Minnesota, and one near Colorado Springs, Colorado, at 2200 m. elevation, had similar behavior patterns in the transplant garden (McMillan, 1959). Population samples of the same six species reached initial flowering over the same 40-day span in Nebraska. When compared under controlled conditions, involving 12½-, 14- and 15½-hour light periods, flowering differences were shown. In *Bouteloua gracilis,* a broader range of tolerance to length of light periods was shown by clones from the Colorado community than by clones from Minnesota which flowered only under the longest light period. In *Panicum virgatum,* both populations responded similarly to 14- and 15½-hour light periods, but differed under shorter periods. The Minnesota clones of Panicum went dormant after a short growth period under 12½-hour light periods, while the Colorado clones grew normally under the same light period but failed to flower.

The community studies support the statement that the simultaneous selection of ecotypic variants within a number of species accounts for the harmony of a given community and its habitat. Natural selection in favoring responses attuned to recurrent habitat sequences has produced vegetational site-climaxes composed of ecotypic variants.

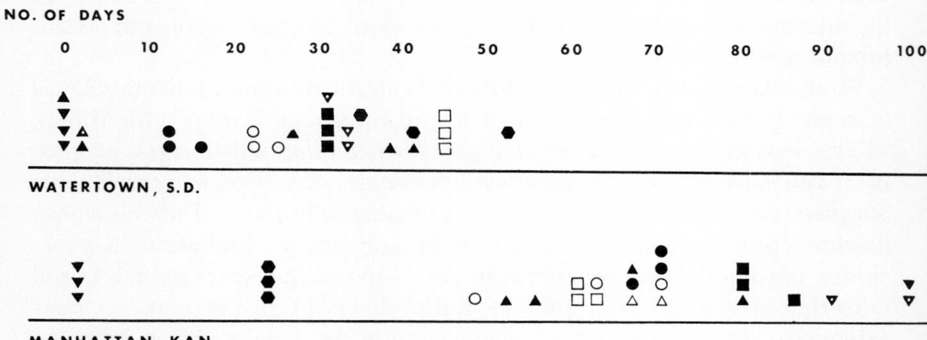

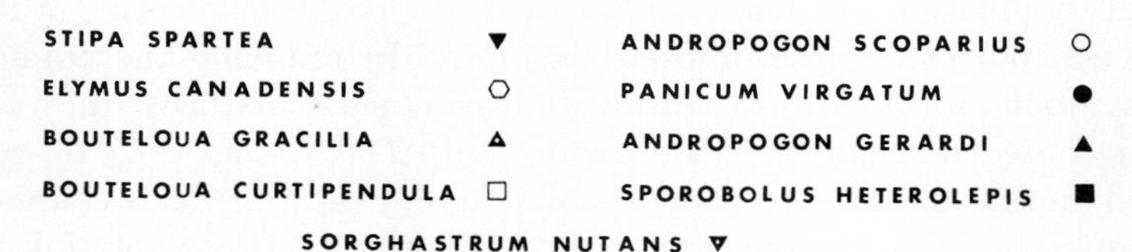

Fig. 1. Responses in a Lincoln, Nebraska, transplant garden. Symbol for each clone indicates the number of days after June 1, 1958, that initial anthesis occurred. For *Stipa spartea*, a late stage of inflorescence development is designated, anthesis is being rarely observed. Two clones of Elymus are from a community directly north of Watertown.

Continuity of a Community-Type

In the investigation of a community-type over a diverse series of habitats, the role of ecotypic variation was studied in the distribution of the characteristic species. In nine grass species of central North America, the wide distribution was shown to result from ecotypic variation (McMillan, 1959). In eight species, *Koeleria cristata, Bouteloua gracilis, Bouteloua curtipendula, Andropogon scoparius, Andropogon gerardi, Panicum virgatun, Sorghastrum nutans,* and *Sporobolus heterolepis,* early maturing types have been selected in northern and high altitude communities. Progressively later maturing types have resulted from the selective pressures of longer growing seasons toward the southeast and at lower elevations. In one (*Elymus canadensis*), early maturity types were from southern communities. In another (*Stipa spartea*), as mentioned above, no behavioral differences characterized the transplanted clones.

A comparison of transplanted clones (McMillan, 1959) indicated the latitudinal and altitudinal trends in community behavior. The community members from Devils Lake, North Dakota, had initial flowering during a span of approximately 40 days. Members of a southern community, Ponca City, Oklahoma, had initial flowering over a period of two and one-half to three times longer. The two communities from intermediate localities, Sioux Falls, South Dakota, and Manhattan, Kansas, showed initial flowering over periods of intermediate length. A similar span of initial flowering dates for communities from three western sites and the Devils Lake site was shown. The comparison involved western sites at progressively higher elevations toward the south, Miles City, Montana (715m.), Wheatland, Wyoming (1480m.), and Peyton, Colorado (near Colorado Springs at 2200m.). Communities along an altitudinal gradient from Peyton, Colorado, to Flagler, Colorado (1500m.) to Hoxie, Kansas (825m.) and to Manhattan, Kansas 310m.) showed a gradient with an increasing span of initial flowering dates toward the lower elevations. In a further comparison of four communities, Fertile, Minnesota, Lincoln, Nebraska, Ponca City, Oklahoma, and Peyton, Colorado, under two different light periods, the essential maturity differences shown in the transplant garden were repeated.

When the communities representing the grassland community-type were transplanted from Nebraska to Texas and studied in the Austin transplant garden during 1959, growth resumption was during late February and early March. At Lincoln, Nebraska, growth resumption by the same clones occurred in late April of 1957 and 1958. The earlier date for growth resumption in Texas yielded actively growing plants under shorter light periods than had been present at a comparable stage of growth in the Nebraska transplant garden. The resulting behavior patterns were partially predicted on the basis of daylength studies, but partially unpredicted because of the previously uninvestigated exposure to a long sequence of increasing daylengths and to sustained high day and high night temperatures. In *Bouteloua gracilis*, clones from the southern communities, capable of flowering under short light periods, flowered earliest. The northern clones, having the earliest maturity patterns under the light-period sequence in the Nebraska transplant garden, were the latest to flower in the Texas garden. The northern clones were unable to flower under the short light periods during the early part of the growing period in central Texas. Dormant pieces of North Dakota clones transplanted from Nebraska to Texas in April flowered at the same time as pieces of the same clones that had been actively growing in Texas since late February. In contrast, dormant pieces of Oklahoma clones transplanted in April flowered later than the pieces of the same clones, which had resumed growth in February. In this material transplanted in April, the flowering pattern in Texas, the Oklahoma clones being later than North

Dakota clones, essentially duplicated the response of these clones in the Nebraska garden. In *Andropogon gerardi,* after a short period of growth in Texas, clones from the more northern communities, entered a dormant stage. Similar behavior had been demonstrated under the shortest light periods in greenhouse studies. After a period of dormancy, as demonstrated in the greenhouse, the clones resumed growth. Following this second growth resumption, the northern clones flowered earliest in Texas, even though the stem height of the earliest flowering culms was mostly under 15–20 cm. Clones from northern communities flowered principally in June and early July; clones from Oklahoma and Texas, in July, August and September. The Texas coast clones flowered latest, in mid-September. In *Bouteloua gracilis* and *Andropogon gerardi* a height gradient was demonstrated in the Texas garden during 1959. The northern clones produced the shortest flowering culms, the mid-latitudinal and high altitude clones produced intermediate-flowering culms, and the clones from Texas produced the tallest culms. In *Panicum virgatum* clones from more northerly locations tended to flower earliest, although much variation occurred among individuals of a population. Certain interpopulational differences were shown that had not been observed in the more northern transplant garden, for example, clones from different populations in Iowa were extremely different in height and behavior. Such differences among the Iowa populations were scarcely observed at the Nebraska transplant garden. Flowering of most Panicum clones from Kansas northward was during May and June. Flowering of Oklahoma and Texas clones extended from July for many Oklahoma and Texas panhandle clones to mid-September for coastal clones. In *Andropogon scoparius* flowering of certain northern clones was in June. In certain of these earliest-flowering clones from North Dakota and South Dakota, the inflorescences barely exceeded the length of the leaves, although later-flowering culms were much longer. Flowering among Texas clones extended into mid-October for coastal types.

These studies support the third statement that the continuity of the grassland community-type over much of Mid-America results from the simultaneous selection of eco-genetic gradients in a number of dominant species. The abstraction of discrete communities into a community-type, such as true prairie, mixed prairie, and coastal prairie, is a convenient method for discussing communities with a particular combination of species. Extreme caution, however, should be exercised in generalizing about the characteristics other than distributional for a community-type.

Although community examples are restricted to the grassland vegetation, natural selection operating within forest and scrub communities has resulted in harmony through variation patterns within many of the component species. The demonstration of ecotypic variation within some of the commonest tree species of North America indicates the significant role of the ecotype in the widespread distribution of a particular kind of forest. Likewise, the demonstration of ecotypic variation in sagebrush indicates that the broad distribution of our western scrub communities may result from the simultaneous selection of eco-genetic gradients within the characteristic species. The continued investigation of the role of the ecotype in community function should prove a profitable ecological pursuit.

Literature Cited

Baker, H. G., 1959, Armeria studies. Carnegie Inst. Washington Yrbk. 48: 103–105.
1953, Race formation and reproductive method in flowering plants. Symposia Soc. Exptl. Biol. 7: 114–145. Cambridge University Press, Cambridge, England.

Böcher, T. W., 1947, Cytogenetic and biological studies in *Geranium robertianum* L. K. Danske Videnskab. Selskab. Biol. Meddel. 20: 1–29.

Bradshaw, A. D., and R. W. Snaydon, 1959, Population differentiation within plant species in response to soil factors. Nature 183: 129–130.

Clausen, J., 1922, Studies on the collective species *Viola tricolor* L. II. Bot. Tidsskr. 37: 363–416.
1926, Genetical and cytological investigations on *Viola tricolor* L. and *V. arvensis* Murr. Hereditas 8: 1–156.

Clausen, J., D. D. Keck and W. M. Hiesey, 1940, Experimental studies on the nature of the species. I. Effect of varied environments on western North American plants. Carnegie Inst. Washington Publ. 520.
1948, Experimental studies on the nature of species. III. Environmental responses of climatic races of Achillea. Carnegie Inst. Washington Publ. 581.

Clausen, J., and W. M. Hiesey, 1958, Experimental studies on the nature of species. IV. Genetic structure of ecological races. Carnegie Inst. Washington Publ. 615.

Clements, F. E., 1936, Nature and structure of the climax. J. Ecol. 24: 252–284.

Cornelius, D. R., 1947, The effect of source of little bluestem grass seed on growth, adaptation, and use in revegetation seedings. J. Agric. Res. 74: 133–143.

Dice, L. R., 1933, Fertility relationships between some of the species and subspecies of mice in the genus Peromyscus. J. Mammal. 14: 298–305.

Dobzhansky, Th., 1948, Genetics of natural populations. XVI. Altitudinal and seasonal changes produced by natural selection in certain populations of *Drosophila pseudoobscura* and *Drosophila persimilis*. Genetics 33: 158–176.

Goldschmidt, R. B., 1934, Lymantria. Bibl. Genetica 11: 1–180.

Goodwin, R. H., 1944, The inheritance of flowering time in a short-day species, *Solidago sempervirens* L. Genetics 29: 503–519.

Gregor, J. W., 1939, Experimental taxonomy. IV. Population differentiation in North American and European sea plantains allied to *Plantago maritima* L.

New Phytol. 38: 293–322.
1944, The ecotype. Biol. Rev. 19: 20–30.
1946, Ecotypic differentiation. New Phytol. 45: 254–270.

Habeck, J. R., 1958, White cedar ecotypes in Wisconsin. Ecology 39: 457–463.

Heiser, C. B., Jr., 1954, Variation and subspeciation in the common sunflower, *Helianthus annuus*. Amer. Midland Nat. 51: 287–305.

Heuts, M. J., 1947, Experimental studies on adaptive evolution in *Gasterosteus aculeatus*. Evolution 1: 89–102.
1949, Racial divergence in fin ray variation patterns in *Gasterosteus aculeatus*. J. Genetics 49: 183–191.

Hiesey, W. M., 1953a, Growth and development of species and hybrids of Poa under controlled temperatures. Amer. J. Bot. 40: 205–221.
1953b, Comparative growth between and within climatic races of Achillea under controlled conditions. Evolution 7: 297–316.

Hovanitz, W., 1945, The combined effect of genetic and environmental variations upon the composition of Colias populations. Ann. Ent. Soc. Amer. 38: 482–502.

Irgens-Moller, H., 1957, Ecotypic response to temperature and photoperiod in Douglas-fir. Forest Sci. 3: 79–83.

Kramer, P. J., 1957, Some effects of various combinations of day and night temperatures and photoperiod on the height growth of loblolly pine seedlings. Forest Sci. 3: 45–55.

Kriebel, H. B., 1957, Patterns of genetic variation in sugar maple. Ohio Agric. Expt. Sta. Res. Bull. 791.

Kruckeberg, A. R., 1951, Intraspecific variability in the response of certain native plant species to serpentine soil. Amer. J. Bot. 38: 408–419.

Kucera, C. L., 1958, Flowering variations in geographic selections of *Eupatorium rugosum* Houtt. Bull. Torrey Bot. Club 85: 40–49.

Langlet, O., 1943, Photoperiodismus und Provenienz bei der gemeinem Kiefer (*Pinus silvestris* L.). Meddel. statens Skogsforsoksanstalt 33: 298–330.

Larsen, E. C., 1947, Photoperiodic responses of geographical strains of *Andropogon scoparius*. Bot. Gaz. 109: 132–149.

Lawrence, W. E., 1945, Some ecotypic relations of *Deschampsia caespitosa*. Amer. J. Bot. 32: 298–314.

McMillan, C., 1957, Nature of the plant community. III. Flowering behavior within two grassland communities under reciprocal transplanting. Amer. J. Bot. 44: 144–153.
1959, The role of ecotypic variation in the distribution of the central grassland of North America. Ecol. Monogr. 29: 285–308.

McMillan, C., and J. Weiler, 1959, Cytogeography of *Panicum virgatum* in Central North America. Amer. J. Bot. 46: 590–593.

Meuli, L. J., and H. L. Shirley, 1937, The effect of seed origin on drought resistance of green ash in the prairie-plains states. J. Forest. 35: 1060–1062.

Moore, J. A., 1944, Geographic variation in *Rana pipiens* Schreber of eastern North America. Bull. Amer. Mus. Nat. Hist. 82: 349–369.
1947, Hybridization between *Rana pipiens* from Vermont and eastern Mexico. Proc. Natl. Acad. Sci. 33: 72–75.

1949, Geographic variation of adaptive characters in *Rana pipiens* Schreber. Evolution 3: 1–24.

Morris, W. G., R. R. Silen and H. Irgens-Moller, 1957, Consistency of bud bursting in Douglas-fir. J. Forest. 55: 208–210.

Nielsen, E. L., 1944, Analysis of variation in *Panicum virgatum*. J. Agric. Res. 69: 327–353.
1947, Polyploidy and winter survival in *Panicum virgatum* L. J. Amer. Soc. Agron. 39: 822–827.

Olmsted, C. E., 1944, Growth and development in range grasses. IV. Photoperiodic responses in twelve geographic strains of side-oats grama. Bot. Gaz. 106: 46–74.

Olson, J. O., F. W. Stearns and H. Nienstaedt, 1959, Eastern hemlock seeds and seedlings. Bull. Connecticut Agric. Expt. Sta. 620.

Pauley, S. S., and T. O. Perry, 1954, Ecotypic variation of the photoperiodic response in Populus. J. Arnold Arboretum 35: 167–188.

Riegel, A., 1940, A study of the variations in the growth of blue grama grass from seed produced in various sections of the Great Plains Region. Trans. Kans. Acad. Sci. 43: 155–171.

Stoeckeler, J. H., and P. O. Rudolf, 1956, Winter coloration and growth of jack pine in the nursery as affected by seed source. Zeitschr. Forstgenetik Forstpflanzenzücht. 5: 161–165.

Turesson, G., 1922, The genotypical response of the plant species to the habitat. Hereditas 3: 211–350.
1925, The plant species in relation to habitat and climate. Hereditas 6: 147–236.

Vaartaja, O., 1959, Evidence of photoperiodic ecotypes in trees. Ecol. Monogr. 29: 91–111.

Ward, G. H., 1953, Artemisia, section Seriphidium in North America. Contr. Dudley Herbarium, Stanford Univ. 4: 155–205.

Weaver, J. E., 1954, North American prairie. 348 pp. Johnsen Publishing Co., Lincoln, Nebr.

Wright, J. W., 1944a, Genotypic variation in white ash. J. Forest. 42: 489–495.
1944b, Ecotypic differentiation in red ash. J. Forest. 42: 591–597.

The Experimental Approach to Problems of Evolution

G. L. Stebbins

During the past twenty five years, the study of organic evolution has taken on new life. This has resulted from the research and discussion of biologists who have applied to evolutionary problems information de-

Reprinted by permission of the author and publisher from *Folia biologica* (Prague), *11:* 1–10, 1965.

rived from several different disciplines: genetics, taxonomy, ecology, paleontology and biochemistry. A series of symposia held five years ago, celebrating the centennial anniversary of the publication of Darwin's *Origin of Species,* revealed a remarkable agreement among participating biologists, who recognized that we now have a basically new and different theory about the processes of evolution, which has been called the modern synthetic theory. The most complete and recent accounts of this theory are *Animal Species and Evolution* by Ernst Mayr, and *The Origin of Adaptations* by Verne Grant.

The modern, synthetic theory resembles Darwin's theory of natural selection in its synthetic nature, since it depends almost equally upon information from several disciplines, but differs from it in two respects. In the first place, it recognizes that the constancy of heredity is based upon the regular transmission of essentially constant, particulate genes, and that the hereditary change on which evolution is based must consist of alterations in these genes. But since most of the gene changes, or mutations, which benefit the population and so become spread through the species have, individually, small effects on the appearance of organism, and these effects can be modified in various ways during the development of the individual, the discontinuity of particulate genes which exists at the level of the geneotype may often become in any population, a continuity of phenotypic expression.

The second difference between Darwinian natural selection and the modern synthetic theory is more in method than in principle. Darwin relied for his information to a large extent upon casual observations and more or less anecdotal accounts which reached him in various ways. In his day, the concept of prediction followed by careful experimentation, with results quantified, was still in a rudimentary stage. Now, however, this method has spread to all fields of scientific investigation, including the processes of evolution. We cannot, of course, conduct experiments which will help us to reconstruct past evolutionary histories, or the ancestry of any particular group. We can, however, conduct as careful experiments as can any other biologists to verify our predictions about the way in which individual processes of evolution go on, and how they interact with each other. This is the phase of evolutionary study which I should like to emphasize today.

The five basic processes of evolution are gene mutation, changes in chromosome structure and number, genetic recombination, natural selection, and reproductive isolation. The first three provide the genetic variability without which change cannot take place. Natural selection and reproductive isolation are processes involving the interaction of organisms with the environment or with each other, which guide populations of organisms into adaptive channels. The more we know about these processes and their interrelationships, the less reason we have for believing that other basic processes remain to be discovered. We do not need any more to search for hidden causes of evolution; we do need to understand much more about the way in which known processes interact with each other. This heightened understanding is likely to come chiefly through performing careful experiments. In the present discussion, I shall give a brief account of some of the most significant experiments of this nature which have been performed and suggest others which need to be done.

As in all fields of modern science, the most significant experiments in the evolutionary field have been those carried out to answer very specific questions, or to verify, if possible, specific predictions. Such general questions as "what is the significance of mutations" or "does natural selection play a creative role," while justifiable to pose for eventual answers, are not the type of question which can be answered by means of one or a few clear-cut experiments. Answers to them must be obtained by the synthetic method, i.e. through piecing together the answers which have previously been obtained to more precise, restricted questions. In a short review such as the present one, I can only single out a few of the appropriate questions and experiments designed to answer them. I have made my sample as representative as possible of the questions which we ask about mutation, genetic recombination, selection, and reproductive isolation.

The Role of Mutations

The first question is as follows. Granted the fact, which now has been demonstrated by numerous experiments, that most mutations with conspicuous effects on the phenotype are deleterious and rejected by selection, can mutations be induced by radiation or any other artificial means which might help adapt a population to a new environment, and so contribute to evolution? If they can, then we might expect that a small proportion of spontaneous mutations will also be adaptive. The obvious way to answer this question would be to produce a number of potentially valuable mutations, to make laboratory or garden populations containing these mutations in high frequency, and to establish some of these populations in sites where they could maintain themselves without human care. Such experiments have not yet been performed. They would require a considerable amount of time and space, but at present we know a number of plant and animal groups which would lend themselves to this kind of experimentation.

A type of experiment which provides a partial answer to this question is the artificial production of valuable mutations in cultivated plants. One could reason logically that a cultivated field is a type of habitat which differs from natural habitats because it is man-made and supported by man, but that intrinsically the difference between the cultivated field and the surrounding wayside is no greater than that between two natural habitats. Consequently, if some mutations can be produced which will make the plant more productive in the field, among the great variety of mutations which appear following radiation or chemical treatment there should be others which would make the plant more productive in a habitat not controlled by man.

Among the numerous examples of experimental production of useful mutations, one of the most extensive is that of Åke Gustafsson of Sweden, carried out over almost twenty years using cultivated barley (*Hordeum vulgare*). Out of hundreds of mutations which he has produced, a small proportion have definitely increased productivity and other valuable characteristics of the barley plant, such as earliness and resistance to lodging. The exact percentage of useful mutations has not been estimated, but it certainly is less than one per cent. In these experiments with barley, as in all others on mutagenesis, more than 99 per cent of mutations, either spontaneous or induced, are detrimental to the organism.

One important point about Gustafsson's experiments is that the useful mutations cannot be regarded as of intrinsic benefit. They do not improve the barley plant under all conditions, but only under those of northern Europe. The most promising of them are the stiff strawed, early types which he designates erectoides. In the moist, cool climate of Sweden, they produce an early plant which is more resistant to lodging, i.e. bending down under the weight of the seed head, than is the variety which gave rise to the mutation. But I am informed by my colleague, Dr. Charles Schaller (personal comm.) that these erectoides types are useless in the hot, dry climate of the central valley of California, because their heads become brittle before the seeds are ripe, and shatter their grain when blown by the wind.

This example plus many others tells us that we cannot expect any single mutation to improve the overall fitness of an organism, but only its adaptation to particular environments. Overall improvements in fitness do occasionally occur during the evolutionary history of a group, such as the acquisition by mammals of warm blood and the elaborate receptor mechanisms formed by the ossicles in the ear. These are, however, very rare as compared to adaptations to specific habitats. Furthermore, all examples of such improved structures about which adequate evidence on the evolutionary history is available have evolved gradually, through the accumulation of many mutations and gene combinations. Individual stages of their evolution existed in restricted groups of animals adapted to particular habitats. From these considerations we can conclude that primary adaptations are always to particular environmental situations, and make use of only a tiny proportion of available mutations. Generalized evolutionary advances occur in those rare instances when a structure or group of structures through a long course of evolution, has evolved to such a degree of perfection that it enables its bearers to radiate from their original, rather specialized niche, into a variety of habitats, and to exploit these habitats in a new way.

A question about the mutation process which cannot be answered by means of experiments with induced mutations is: Which have played the largest role as components of evolutionary change, individual mutations with large effects on the phenotype, or large numbers of mutations, each one having a small effect on the phenotype? As with all questions involving evolutionary history, this one can be answered only by indirect means. We can, however, make the following inferences. If, in a progeny from hybrids between two natural populations, a particular character segregates according to a recognizable Mendelian ratio, we can infer that this character difference is determined by one or a small number of genes, and hence arose through the occurrence and establishment of one or a small number of mutations, each of them with a conspicuous effect on the phenotype. If, on the other hand, segregation for a particular character is not according to a well defined ratio, but forms a blending pattern, with a mode intermediate between the parents, then we can infer that many genes contribute to the difference. It has, therefore, originated gradually through the establishment of many mutations, each with a small effect on the phenotype.

Many examples are now available of hybrids between different races in species of both animals and plants. One of the most extensive is that of Clausen and Hiesey on the Californian plant species *Potentilla glandulosa*. They studied two large progenies of hybrids between alpine and lowland races of this species, which differ in a large number of characters of both vegetative and reproductive organs. Most of the character differences between these races, such as winter dormancy, leaf size and shape, stem height, branching, and pubescence, are determined by so many different gene pairs that their number could not be estimated. Others, such as petal color and notching, are determined by two, three, or four gene pairs. The only possible inference which we can draw from these data and many others like them is that the races of *Potentilla* diverged gradually, through the accumulation and establishment of a large number of genetic differences. The fact must be further emphasized that the differences between the alpine and foothill races of *Potentilla glandulosa* in such taxonomically significant characteristics as size and shape of sepals and petals, and size, shape and color of fruits (achenes) is just as great as it is between many perfectly valid species of *Potentilla*. The only reason why these extreme races cannot be recognized as species is that they are completely interfertile, and many races intermediate between them exist in nature. We can infer, therefore, that the morphological and ecological character differences which separate species as well as races in these plants originate largely through the accumulation of many genetic differences with small effects, rather than a few "macromutations" with conspicuous effects on the phenotype.

There are, however, conspicuous exceptions to this rule. Although they are uncommon, these exceptions may have an evolutionary significance far out of proportion to the rarity of their occurrence. An example in animals will be presented later, in a discussion of the origin of mimicry.

In plants, a good example has been provided by the experiments of Prazmo on hybridization between species of *Aquilegia.* The most familiar species of this genus, *A. vulgaris,* has violet petals bearing curved spurs, which contain nectar. These adapt the flower to pollination by bumblebees (*Bombus*). The two most common North American species, *A. canadensis* in the east and *A. formosa* in the west, have red flowers with slender straight spurs, which are pollinated by hummingbirds (Colibris). Another group of species in western North America, with white, pale blue, or pale yellow flowers bearing very long, straight spurs, are pollinated by sphingid moths. Consequently, the differentiation of the genus *Aquilegia* from other genera of Ranunculaceae, as well as the formation of species within the genus, has depended primarily on the origin and diversification of the spur-bearing petals, which have adapted the flowers to various specialized pollinators.

A single species of eastern Asia, *Aquilegia ecalcarata,* provides a link between Aquilegia and other genera of Ranunculaceae, since its petals lack spurs. Prazmo has made hybrids between *A. ecalcarata* and *A. vulgaris,* which are partly fertile. The F_1 plants had well developed spurs on their petals, and in an F_2 progeny of 202 plants, a clear segregation of 3 spurred to 1 spurless was found. In other characteristics, however, such as plant height, leaf shape, size and shape of sepals, length of spurs, and seed size, segregations typical of multifactorial differences were found. In later research, a similar segregation ratio was found in hybrids between *A. canadensis* and *A. ecalcarata,* but the gene for spurs of *A. canadensis* segregates independently of that found in *A. vulgaris.* The moth pollinated species *A. chrysantha* contains both genes.

From these experiments and observations we can infer that the most distinctive characteristic of the genus Aquilegia, the spurred petal, evolved through the occurrence and establishment of two mutations with conspicuous effects on the phenotype. The change from pollination by unspecialized insects to adaptation for pollination by such specialized vectors as bumblebees, hummingbirds, and moths, probably took place abruptly, lifting the progenitor of *Aquilegia* to new levels of adaptation. Subsequently, adaptive radiation within the genus was accomplished by the more usual process of the accumulation of many genetic differences with small effects, guided by natural selection.

The Adaptive Value of Gene Combinations

Once we recognize that most evolutionary changes are accomplished by building up adaptive combinations of many genes, we realize that the mechanisms by which genes are combined, and favorable gene combinations retained intact within the population, are of primary importance in evolution. The experimental study of these mechanisms has been one of the most extensively worked and fruitful fields of modern evolutionary research. Through his studies of inversions in chromosomes of *Drosophila pseudoobscura*, Dobzhansky (1951) first recognized the evolutionary importance of chromosomal rearrangements in natural populations. They serve to tie together and transmit as units adaptive combinations of genes.

Dobzhansky's experiments were preceded by observations and comparisons similar to those ordinarily used for evolutionary studies. Using the giant salivary chromosomes as morphological guide posts, he detected several different inversion types or gene arrangements which occur in similar frequencies in adjacent and similarly adapted populations, and of which the frequencies vary in a regular fashion throughout the range of the species. He therefore made the working hypothesis that a particular complex of inversions, in respect both to the types present and their frequency, adapts a population to a particular set of climatic conditions, and that the regular variation in frequency of inversion types which is found throughout the range of the species is a reflection of its adaptation to a highly diverse series of climatic conditions. In most populations of *Drosophila pseudoobscura* the frequencies of inversions remain essentially constant throughout the year. In one locality in the mountains of Southern California, however, (Piñon Flats), a marked and regular seasonal fluctuation in the frequency of two inversions was detected. This gave Dobzhansky an opportunity to test his hypothesis experimentally. Using the population cage method developed by L'Héritier and Teissier, he found that under conditions somewhat similar to those which prevail in summer at the natural locality, i.e. a temperature of 25° and a high population density, the proportions of two inversions (Standard and Chiricahua) become stabilized after about four months at frequencies of 70 per cent of one and 30 per cent of the other, no matter what was their initial frequency among the flies introduced into the cage. This resembles closely the frequency of the two types during the summer in the natural locality. In a later experiment, Birth (1955) found that flies raised in population cages at the same temperature but a low population density established an equilibrium similar to that prevailing in spring at the natural locality, i.e. 30 per cent of Standard and 70 per cent of Chiricahua. In both of these experiments, heterozygotes for the two chromosomal arrangements occurred in a higher frequency than would be expected, according to the Hardy-Weinberg law, on the basis of random mating and additive effects of genes. Consequently, heterozygotes for these chromosomal segments must have been better adapted than either homozygote to the conditions of the population cages.

From these experiments and many others like them, we can draw the following conclusions. Not only individual characteristics, but also combinations of characteristics, as well as the ability to generate such combinations and to retain them in populations, have differential adaptive values, and so will come to differ between differently adapted populations. Furthermore, interactions between genes are such that heterozygous combinations are often adaptively superior to combinations of the same genes in the homozygous state. Consequently in many, perhaps most populations, natural selection does not act separately upon individual gene differences, but simultaneously upon interacting combinations of genes. Some genes or gene combinations are retained in populations not because of their intrinsic adaptive value per se, but because of favourable interactions with other genes, or between different genotypes in the populations. Further experimental tests of this hypothesis have been made more recently by Beardnore, Dobzhansky and Pavlovsky (1960) who showed that chromosomally polymorphic populations of *Drosophila pseudoobscura* produce more individuals and a greater biomass than monomorphic populations.

Such experimental findings have led to the concept that the individual is not the basic unit of selection, but merely the temporary home of a combination of more permanent genes. The evolutionary significance of the individual may lie as much in the genetic contribution which he makes to the population as in his own intrinsic adaptive value. From the standpoint of evolution over many generations, the more significant unit of selection, as Dobzhansky (1957) has pointed out, is the Mendelian population of interbreeding individuals.

The Nature and Limits of Natural Selection

The hypothesis of Charles Darwin, that the principal guiding process of evolution is natural selection, which can be defined as the interaction between populations and their environment to produce differential reproduction of certain genes or gene combinations, has now been tested experimentally in a great variety of ways. In simple populations of microorganisms, progressive adaptation to high concentrations of antibiotic substances in the medium, by successive steps of mutation and selection, has been demonstrated by Demerec, Cavalli and Maccacaro, and others. Furthermore, Kettlewell has shown by appropriate quantitative experiments that dramatic changes in frequency of certain melanic genotypes of moths in the industrial regions of England have been guided by natural selection, due to the fact that melanic types are better protected against predators in industrial regions and pale types are better protected in unaltered forests of non-industrial regions. Additional experiments have provided at least partial answers to three other questions of great importance to the theory of natural selection.

The first of these questions is: To what extent does the unavailability of genetic variation place a limitation upon natural selection? An elaborate experiment by Reeve and Robertson on artificial selection for wing length in *Drosophila melanogaster* suggests that in this species the limiting factor is not genetic variation per se, but the physiological and adaptive inferiority of extreme variants. A wild strain was selected during 76 generations for long wings. A definite response to selection occurred over the first twenty generations and a much slower response up to the 46th generation, but from then on the population did not respond at all to selection. Nevertheless, during this whole period it retained about the same amount of variability, which was considerably greater than that of the wild ancestral population. Furthermore, both relaxed selection and reversed selection at various periods produced a reversion toward the original wing length. Tests of viability showed that the unstable equilibrium which was maintained during the later generations of selection was due to the poor viability and low fertility of extreme longwinged variants. Whether this inferiority was due to adverse pleiotropic effects of genes responsible for long wings, or to semi-lethal genes linked with them, could not be determined. At any rate, this experiment and several others like it suggest that at least in cross fertilizing populations the limits on natural selection are rarely, if ever, set by a lack of appropriate genetic variability.

A quantitative experimental study of Imam and Allard (1965) on natural populations of *Avena fatua* in California has revealed a large amount of unsuspected genetic variability in them in spite of the fact that the species is largely self-pollinating. This variability is maintained partly through occasional outcrossing, and partly through heterozygosity for chromosomal segments marked by recognizable genes. This species is able to respond both to variations in the climate of different parts of California, and to microhabitat differences within an area by selection for differentially adaptive gene combinations.

The second question is: How can natural selection guide populations toward the intricate and elaborate adaptive mechanisms which are the wonder of all naturalists who have seen them? A partial answer to this question has been provided by two series of recent experiments on mimicry. The first of these, conducted by L. P. and J. v. Z. Brower have shown that mimicry can actually protect insects against predators which have been conditioned to avoid the noxious models. In one experiment

(Brower, Brower and Wescott, 1960) they conditioned captive toads to avoid bees through exposure to their stings. These toads avoided equally Asilid flies, which superficially resemble bees, but readily ate dragonflies (*Pachydiplax*) throughout the experiment. Control toads which had not been exposed to bee stings readily ate both Asilid flies and bees from which the sting had been removed. Other experiments by the Browers with starlings have demonstrated the effectiveness both of the mimicry of one butterfly species by another and artificial "mimics" of artificially noxious "models" produced by painting meal worms with either bitter or palatable colored paint.

A second series of experiments dealing with mimicry has been conducted by Clarke and Sheppard (1960a, b, c, 1964) on the African swallowtail butterfly *Papilio dardanus*, the females of which mimic various species of the family Danaidae, all of which have a noxious taste, and in experiments by the Browers and others have been demonstrated to be rejected by birds. In Ethiopia and Madagascar, where models of the family Danaidae do not occur, both males and females of *P. dardanus* are nonmimicking. In central Africa, there occur nine different mimicking forms of females, which resemble six different species of Danaidae. Genetic experiments have shown that these forms segregate in simple Mendelian fashion, and are apparently determined by a "super gene," or chromosomal segment of closely linked loci. They differ somewhat in their geographic distributions, but overlap to such an extent that any race of *P. dardanus* in central Africa contains up to four or five sympatric mimicking forms of females.

In crosses between forms inhabiting the same area, the segregation of the progeny is clear-cut, complete dominance exists, and only typical, perfect mimics of one type or another appear in the progeny. If, however, crosses are made between allopatric forms, which have never been in genetic contact with each other, the F_1 hybrid is usually intermediate. The variation between different F_1 individuals of the same cross is considerable, while the F_2 or back cross progeny do not show clear-cut segregations. The evidence from these genetic experiments supports, therefore, an hypothesis developed many years ago by R. A. Fisher. Mimicry originated in *P. dardanus* through the occurrence and establishment of mutation with a conspicuous effect on the color and general outline of the wing, giving it a crude resemblance to one of the noxious models. Subsequently, additional mutations at closely linked loci perfected the pattern, and further mutations at the same locus made possible the perfection of forms mimicking other models. Between sympatric forms which frequently intercross, a large number of modifier genes has been fixed by natural selection, which bring about a clear-cut segregation of their hybrid progeny. If the forms occur in different regions, however, they have not had an opportunity to cross, so that modifiers affecting their segregation ratios have not become established.

The resemblance between the genetic basis and the probable origin of this array of mimicking forms of a butterfly and the diversity of flower types in *Aquilegia* is striking. It suggests that the usual mode of origin of such precise and remarkable adaptations is through the initial establishment of a "switch" mutation or gene combination, which lifts the population abruptly out of its previous adaptive groove and into a new, imperfectly developed mode of adaptation. Once this has been accomplished, further action of natural selection on additional genetic variability perfects and diversifies this new adaptive system.

The third question about which new experimental evidence is available is the following: are the mutations and gene combinations which provide the genetic variability upon which natural selection acts always at random relative to the environment of the population, or can phenotypic variation occur in such a way that it facilitates selection in a particular adaptive direction? Recent experiments by Waddington on the phenomenon which he has designated genetic assimilation indicate that the latter may be true in some instances. One example is selection for enlarged anal papillae in the larvae of *Drosophila* (Waddington, 1960). These papillae regulate the osmotic pressure of the body fluids, and tend to get larger by phenotypic modification when larvae are raised in media containing sublethal concentrations of salt, in which only 20 to 30 per cent of the larvae survive. The degree to which this character can be modified phenotypically is under genetic control. Consequently, when cultures of *Drosophila* were raised for 21 generations in this medium without the practise of any artificial selection, the final stocks were significantly more resistant to salt than were the initial stocks, and had correspondingly enlarged anal papillae. Apparently, natural selection for modifiability of the papillae in response to salt was followed by selection for genes which fixed the papillae at a large size.

Genetic assimilation, though only a form of natural selection which relies upon a previously existing and genetically variable modifiability of the phenotype, is nevertheless a mechanism by which populations may, under conditions of environmental stress, pass more readily from one adaptive peak to another than they could if they had to rely upon rare mutations with small effects, completely at random with reference to a particular environmental change. It could have initiated a number of familiar adaptations, such as succulence in certain desert and seashore plants, and increase horn or tooth size in some mammals.

The Experimental Origin and Establishment of Species

Experiments to analyze the nature of reproductive isolation, the final one of the basic evolutionary processes, have been very numerous, consisting of hybridizations between species, subspecies, and "semi-species" in various groups of animals and plants. I do not have time to review any examples here, but can refer you to two recent books on the subject: *Animal Species and Evolution* by Ernst Mayr (1963) and *The Origin of Adaptations* by Verne Grant (1963). I should like to conclude this talk by describing two of my own experiments on the synthesis of reproductively isolated populations, and their establishment under natural conditions.

In higher plants, the quickest way to produce a barrier which will effectively block gene exchange between a newly synthesized population and its progenitors is by doubling the chromosome number to produce a polyploid. Such polyploids have been produced many times in the laboratory and garden. Some of them have entered commercial production as new varieties of crop plants or horticultural ornamentals. Relatively few, however, have been used for experiments on evolution, by their establishment under natural conditions. I should like to describe two examples.

The first concerns a species of grass from South Africa, *Ehrharta erecta,* which became established on the University of California campus before 1940. In 1942, I treated seeds from these adventive plants with colchicine, and obtained an autotetraploid with 48 as the somatic chromosome number, in contrast to 24 in the original diploid. Seeds of both diploid and tetraploid were planted in 1943, in several semi-wild woodland areas above the campus. Two of these have been particularly successful, since in both of them, the species has now spread from the original 5-meter square plots to cover more than an acre of ground, forming the dominant herbaceous cover in much of the area occupied. In both of them the diploid is more abundant and widespread than the tetraploid, and in one, the tetraploid has almost completely disappeared. In the other (plot 7c), the tetraploid was more abundant than the diploid for the first ten years after establishment, as reported earlier (Stebbins, 1949) but recently the diploid has been spreading more rapidly. The most striking fact, however, it is that the two chromosomal types are occupying distinctly different microhabitats. The tetraploid is now most abundant in an area about 10 meters square, 100 meters below the original planting site. This spot is in the deep shade of an oak tree, in loose, well-drained soil. Immediately adjacent to it is a recently established area of diploid plants, which are in a somewhat sunny part of the hill. Throughout the area, the diploid is most abundant in partial shade, where the soil is more firmly packed and relatively moist in winter, while the tetraploid is found only in the deepest shade and in well drained soil. Although hundreds of plants have been examined, none of them has had the sterility and intermediate characteristics which would be expected in a triploid. The diploid and tetraploid population are, therefore, effectively isolated from each other, even when intermingled.

In this semi-natural habitat the tetraploid can readily be distinguished from the diploid by its coarser, more bluish leaves, stouter panicle branches and larger seeds. It has maintained itself in competition with the natural vegetation for twenty years, and is still spreading. Because of differences in microhabitat adaptation, diploid and tetraploid populations compete with each other to only a limited degree. Consequently the artificial tetraploid possesses distinct morphological characteristics, is reproductively isolated from all populations with which it is in contact, is successful in a distinctive habitat not subject to direct human interference and so has all of the characteristics usually associated with a valid species.

The second example is an amphiploid produced by doubling the chromosome number of a hybrid between two species of grasses which are usually placed in separate genera, *Elymus glaucus* and *Sitanion jubatum*. The undoubled F_1 hybrid between these two species is frequent as a wild plant in California, since the two parental species occur together in many places, and hybridize rather easily. In spite of the fact that both of the parental species have the same chromosome number, $2n = 28$, and the hybrid, like its parents, forms 14 bivalents at meiosis, this hybrid is completely sterile (Stebbins, Valencia and Valencia, 1946). The doubled F_1 hybrid, with $2n = 56$ chromosomes, is about 80 per cent fertile, but its progeny segregate for varying degrees of sterility. Morphologically, however, they breed true for the intermediate condition of the F_1 hybrid (Stebbins and Vaarama, 1954).

In 1952, seeds of this amphiploid were sown in a number of wild areas in the foothills surrounding the Central Valley of California. Successful establishment was obtained on a hillside about fifty miles northwest of Davis. Although the population is still small, it has survived in this spot for ten years, and a visit this spring disclosed the presence of several seedlings which had come up last winter. Here, also, is a population which has all of the characteristics of a distinct species, and which has been successfully established under essentially natural conditions.

The experiments which I have described are only a small sample of those performed. I hope, however, that they have demonstrated the principal point which I want to make. Organic evolution is as valid a field as any other in the biological sciences in which to conduct precise, quantitative experiments. Most of these must necessarily be designed to analyse processes which have gone on in the past and are still going on. As our knowledge increases, however, we should be able to design an increasingly large number of experiments of a synthetic nature. We should be able to make evolution go before our eyes, to watch, and even to direct, its progress.

References

Beardmore, J. A., Dobzhansky, Th., Pavlovsky, O. A.: *An attempt to compare the fitness of polymorphic and monomorphic experimental populations of Drosophila pseudoobscura.* Heredity, *14* : 19, 1960.

Birch, L. C.: *Selection in Drosophila pseudoobscura in relation to crowding.* Evolution, 9 : 389, 1955.

Brower, J. van Zandt: *Experimental studies of mimicry. IV. The reactions of starlings to different proportions of models and mimics.* Amer. Nat., *94* : 271, 1960.

Brower, L. P., Brower, J. van Zandt, Westcott, Peter W.: *Experimental studies of mimicry. V. The reactions of toads (Bufo terrestris) to bumblebees (Bombus americanorum) and their robberfly mimics (Mallophora bomboides) with a discussion of aggressive mimicry.* Amer. Nat., *94* : 343, 1960.

Cavalli, L. L., Maccaro, G. A.: *Polygenic inheritance of drug resistance in the bacterium Escherichia coli.* Heredity, *6* : 311, 1952.

Clarke, C. A., Sheppard, P. M.: *The evolution of dominance under disruptive selection.* Heredity, *14* : 73, 1960a.

Clarke, C. A., Sheppard, P. M.: *The evolution of mimicry in the butterfly Papilio dardanus.* Heredity, *14* : 163, 1960b.

Clarke, C. A., Sheppard, P. M.: *Super-genes and mimicry.* Heredity, *14* : 175, 1960c.

Clarke, C. A., Sheppard, P. M.: *Interactions between major genes and polygenes in the determination of the mimetic patterns of Papilio dardanus.* Evolution, *17* : 404, 1964.

Clausen J., Hiesey, W. M.: *Experimental studies on the nature of species. IV. Genetic structure of ecological races.* Carnegie Inst. Wash. Publ., 1958 (p. 615).

Demerec, M.: *Production of Staphylococcus strains resistant to various concentrations of penicillin.* Proc. Nat. Acad. Sci., *31* : 16, 1945.

Dobzhansky, Th.: *Genetics and the origin of species.* New York 1951.

Dobzhansky, Th.: *Mendelian populations as genetic systems.* Cold Spring Harbor Symp. on Quant. Biol., *22* : 385, 1957.

Grant, Verne: *Isolation and hybridization between Aquilegia formosa and A. pubescens.* El Aliso, 2 : 341, 1952.

Grant, Verne: *The origin of adaptations.* New York 1963.

Gustafsson, A.: *The induction of early mutants in Bonus barley.* Hereditas, *46* : 675, 1960.

Imam, A. G., Allard, R. W.: *Population studies in predominantly self-pollinated species. VI. Genetic variability between and within natural populations of wild oats, Avena fatua L. from different habitats in California.* Genetics, *51* : 49, 1965.

Kettlewell, H. B. D.: *A resumé of investigations on the evolution of melanism in the Lepidoptera.* Proc. Royal Soc., B.: *145* : 297, 1956.

Mayr, E.: *Animal species and evolution.* Harvard 1963.

Prazmo, W.: *Genetic studies on the genus Aquilegia L. I. Crosses between Aquilegia vulgaris L. and Aquilegia ecalcarata Maxim.* Acta Soc. Bot. Polon., *29* : 57, 1960.

Reeve, E. C. R., Robertson, F. W.: *Studies in quantitative inheritance. II. Analysis of a strain of Drosophila melanogaster selected for long wings.* J. Genet., *51* : 276, 1953.

Stebbins, G. L.: *The evolutionary significance of natural and artificial polyploids in the family Gramineae.* Proc. 8th International Congr. Genet. 1949 (p. 461).

Stebbins, G. L., Valencia, J. I., Valencia, R. M.: *Artificial and natural hybrids in the Gramineae, tribe Hordeae; I. Elymus, Sitanion and Agropyron.* Amer. J. Bot., 33 : 338, 1946.

Stebbins, G. L., Vaarama, A.: *Artificial and natural hybrids in the Gramineae, tribe Hordeae. VII. Hybrids and allopolyploids between Elymus glaucus and Sitanion spp.* Genetics, 39 : 378, 1954.

Waddington, C. H.: *Evolutionary adaptation.* In: *Evolution after Darwin. I. The evolution of life.* Ed. Tax, S. 1960 (p. 381).

Natural Selection and Ecological Theory

Gordon H. Orians

A long and intense controversy over the mechanisms of control of animal populations in nature has accompanied the development of ecology as a vigorous science during the past two decades. While admitting that this has stimulated a great deal of research, I shall argue that much of the controversy has involved peripheral issues and that its perpetuation will continue to result in wasted efforts on the part of ecologists and will add to the confusion among interested non-ecological biologists as to what ecologists are really concerned about. Many share the view of Dobzhansky as expressed during one of the discussions at the Cold Spring Harbor Symposium on Population Studies (1957). "To a non-ecologist, the controversy which has made our session so lively is, I confess, somewhat bewildering. I have had a feeling for several years now that this is a controversy chiefly about words, about 'semantics,' to use a fashionable word. Having tried to the best of my abilty to understand the issue involved, I still continue to feel that way."

In advancing the view that there is really a basic issue involved, which is much deeper than its peripheral manifestation in the form of the argument over density-dependence and density-independence, I shall base my case largely on two important books on population ecology, those of Lack (1954) and Andrewartha and Birch (1954). Recognizing that no two books can effectively speak for an entire field, I still select this course because of the great impact of these books on current thinking and because their views are clearly stated. As with most arguments, the most critical portion concerns the initial assumptions upon which theories are erected. Hence, attention will be concentrated upon these fundamental

Reprinted by permission of the author and publisher from *The American Naturalist, 96:* 257–63, 1962.

assumptions, rather than upon corollaries which follow if the assumptions are granted.

The basic goals of ecology are seldom stated clearly by ecologists, if, indeed, most ecologists even have opinions about them, but Andrewartha and Birch are characteristically explicit on this point. To them it is the job of the ecologist to explain why a certain animal is found in one place and not in another, why it is more numerous in one place than another, and why there are fluctuations in its numbers. To accomplish this, a three-pronged approach is proposed—the physiology and behavior of the animal must be investigated; the physiography, climate, soil, and vegetation of the area must be studied; and the numbers of individuals in the population in question must be measured as accurately as possible. Other organisms are to be investigated as they appear important in the ecology of the species under special investigation.

This method of study is not only presented as being extremely profitable, but also as being definitely preferable to other methods commonly employed by ecologists. Community studies, which are motivated by the hope that predictable relationships between the relative abundance and interactions of species can be discovered leading to insights into community structure, are rejected as having contributed nothing, and as being unlikely to contribute anything in the future, to general theory. When too much attention is put upon the community, too little attention is paid to the species whose distribution and abundance are to be explained. Moreover, the community studies are said to stress the importance of other plants and animals to the neglect of other components of the environment.

In my view, the rejection of community ecology by Andrewartha and Birch is the corollary of a still more basic position, namely, that evolutionary concepts have no place in ecological theory. The importance of natural selection is not disputed, for the final section of the book is devoted to evolutionary aspects of ecology, and Birch (1955, 1961) has made important contributions to the study of evolution. Rather it is claimed that a general and satisfying theory of ecology can and should be constructed without recourse to evolutionary thinking and concepts. This view is clearly illustrated by the now famous case of the bees in the auger-holes (page 23). It is the job of the ecologist to count auger-holes and so to predict the number of bees to be found and the job of the evolutionist to measure genetic change as a result of competition. Conceptually, the two fields are kept quite distinct.

Their general theory of ecology states that the numbers of animals in natural populations may be limited in three ways: (1) by shortage of material resources, (2) by inaccessibility of resources, and (3) by the short period of time in which the intrinsic rate of natural increase (r) is positive. The fact that the third of these factors belongs to a category quite distinct from the first two need not be pursued now. For the present it is sufficient to note that, unfortunately, the current controversy is centered around the relative importance of these factors and not upon the assumptions which have led to them.

Lack does not attempt to state a formal theory of ecology but his approach to ecological problems is clearly outlined in the introduction to the book. Since the book is oriented toward population control, Lack does not consider community studies, but there is an implicit acceptance of their fundamental importance. On points other than those pertaining to communities, he is clear. The distinguishing feature of his approach to ecology is an emphasis upon the need to recognize the distinction between proximate and ultimate factors. Believing that ultimate factors provide the key to the understanding of current population adaptations, Lack has oriented his own research toward the elucidation of evolutionary mechanisms in ecology. Andrewartha and Birch are, of necessity, concerned only with proximate factors and it is at this point that the most fundamental dichotomy exists.

Lack also strongly supports the belief that controlling mortality factors must be density-dependent. He thus rejects climate *per se* as a controlling mechanism and discusses climate only with respect to changes in range and not with respect to population regulation. In contrast, Andrewartha and Brich ascribe major importance to control of populations by climate and regard distribution and abundance as two aspects of the same problem.

Given these striking differences in viewpoint, it remains to analyze their significance. Since Lack has studied primarily birds and Andrewartha and Birch, insects, it is fruitful to consider whether the differences in viewpoint might be attributable to their choice of organisms since it is to be expected that different organisms will have differing autecologies. It is important to note, however, that Andrewartha does not believe this to be the case, for in his recent book (1961) he is at great pains to cite vertebrate examples, conspicuous by their absence in the earlier book, to substantiate views derived from studies of insects.

Despite this, however, several major possibilities immediately suggest themselves. First, insects are heterothermic and therefore more at the direct mercy of climatic variations than homeothermic birds which can stand wide variations in climate provided resources are available, especially in desert or near-desert environments. Second, a large proportion of insects which have been intensively studied are herbivores, whereas most birds are insectivores or carnivores. Since the apparent inability of herbivores to make effective use of the primary productivity in most terrestrial ecosystems is a puzzling problem, it could be argued that control mechanisms in herbivores are basically different (Hairston, Smith and Slobodkin, 1960). From this it might follow that orderly predictions about insect populations are more difficult to make and, hence, such populations are more appropriately treated by different methods (MacArthur, 1961). Moreover, most birds exhibit well-defined territorial behavior which may act strongly as a density-regulating factor (Orians, 1961), thus modifying the impact of the population upon its resources to a much greater degree than in insects with less highly developed intrapopulational control mechanisms. However, this argument ignores the complexity of the problem of utilization of primary productivity in terrestrial ecosystems. The assumption of different control mechanisms for herbivores and carnivores is based upon inadequate evidence and fails to consider the problem of food quality, often of prime importance to herbivores (Cowan et al., 1950; Taber, 1956, Harlan, 1956; Orians and Pitelka, 1960). Moreover, though the action of natural selection may be more difficult to trace in insect populations than birds, this provides no convincing basis for rejecting an evolutionary approach.

Further, we may consider differences in the nature of the communities studied by field ecologists. As economic entomologists, primarily concerned with insect pests of croplands and their predators, Andrewartha and Birch work in the highly artificial and recently derived communities of pure-stand crops. One result is that most insects are studied not in the native vegetation to which they have been evolutionarily adapted but in recently colonized habitats many of which are geographically remote from the natural range of the species. In most cases nothing is known of the ecology of the species in diversified natural communities so that the adaptive significance of many life history features is obscure. It is at present impossible to assess the impact of these circumstances in relation to empirical results on population fluctuations in cropland pests, but there is clearly sufficient ground for caution in generalizing from these results to natural communities. Moreover, the growth of economic entomology has been stimulated by particular practical demands, namely the prediction of outbreaks of pests and their control, either through predators or through the discovery of a particularly vulnerable stage of the life history. Since correlation may permit prediction, these goals can often be achieved by obtaining climatic correlations with population fluctuations, despite the fact that the correlation need not imply causation.

However important the differences in the autecologies and environments of organisms studied by ecologists of different schools of thought may be, I believe that the fundamental dichotomy in modern ecology, as illustrated by the books under consideration, can only be understood as a manifestation of the fundamental division of biology into two major categories—functional biology and evolutionary biology (Mayr, 1961). The differences in method and basic concepts of these major fields is sharply focused in this controversy though its roots have apparently not been grasped either by the participants or interested observers. As functional ecologists, Andrewartha and Birch are concerned with the operation and interaction of populations and one of their major concerns is with experimental control of environmental variables. This approach leads to the rejection of results directed toward the elucidation of the action of natural selection upon populations, such as the distribution of chaffinches (*Fringilla coelebs and F. coerulea*) in the Canary Islands (Lack and Southern, 1949) and character displacement (Vaurie, 1951; Brown and Wilson, 1956). To the evolutionary ecologist, this rejection is quite inconsistent with their easy acceptance of climatic correlations that appear far less ciritical and may easily be misinterpreted through improper application of statistics (Smith, 1961).

As an evolutionary ecologist, Lack is primarily concerned with the causes behind observable ecological adaptations and has made his major contribution in the subject of the evolution of reproductive rates. This approach leads to the rejection of climate as a significant regulating factor for populations, a rejection which the functional ecologist finds incomprehensible.

It is pointless to debate the validity of these contrasting approaches to ecology as both have clearly justified their usefulness in all fields of biology. However, it is of great importance to consider the claim of Andrewartha and Birch that general ecological theory can and should be built solely upon the functional approach. Just as many physiologists treat the animal body as a highly interesting and complex mechanism which has not been and is not going anywhere, Andrewartha and Birch treat ecology as the study of complex relationships between animal populations and their environments which are to be best understood as neither having evolved nor continuing to evolve.

It is becoming increasingly apparent that a complete answer to any question should deal with physiological, adaptational and evolutionary aspects of the problem (Pittendrigh, 1958). The evolutionary process of becoming yields the most profound understanding of biological systems at all levels of organization (Simpson, Pittendrigh and Tiffany, 1957). The non-evolutionary answer to the question of why an animal is abundant in some parts of its range and rare in others is of necessity incomplete. The functional ecologist can and does make an important contribution to the understanding of the dynamics of populations, but for the formulation of theory it is essential that the approaches be combined. The functional approach by itself cannot provide a basis for theory and, in fact, the "theory" of Andrewartha and Birch really states that no general theory of ecology is possible and that each case must be considered individually, which is really a statement of research technique rather than theory.

The application of selectionist thinking to natural populations has already led to deeper insights about the proximate relationships of populations. In fact, it is difficult to think about populations without considering the selective advantage of various life history features. Lack's work on avian reproductive rates is an excellent example of ecological insight derived from selectionist thinking. Another is R. A. Fisher's theory on the evolution of sex ratios, originally proposed in 1930 and recently amplified by Kolman (1960) and Bodmer and Edwards (1960). To this we may add Medawar's (1957) stimulating discussion of the evolution of death rates, a fundamental ecological and physiological problem; all competition studies; the ecology of vertebrate social organization (Pitelka, 1959; Orians, 1960, 1961); and the nature of animal niches (Hutchinson, 1959; MacArthur, 1961). Recent studies of species abundance and diversity (Kohn, 1959; MacArthur, 1957, 1960; MacArthur and MacArthur, 1961) are also producing promising results, but it still is too early to evaluate them adequately. Also, animal ecologists are adopting more widely the community approach which has been intensively and extensively used by plant ecologists for decades (Elton, 1949).

On the other hand, Lack and others of similar viewpoint probably overstate the case for density-dependence when they assume that regulation and evolution cannot occur unless there is so-called biological control and competition. The role of climate as a controlling mechanism is often doubted on this ground alone, but Birch (1960) has made a valid claim for the operation of natural selection through climate. Moreover, environments do fluctuate and may do so regularly enough to prevent competition from proceeding to its conclusion (Hutchinson. 1953).

Finally, it may be asked whether or not there is any such thing as a general theory of ecology, satisfying or unsatisfying. Is there a theory of behavior or comparative anatomy or embryology or physiology? Whereas there are descriptive generalizations in all of these fields, the only general theory which now seems possible is that of natural selection. Ecology, too, has its descriptive generalizations, such as the principle of competitive exclusion, but as in other fields, evolution would seem to be the only real theory of ecology today. Even if one strongly believes in the action of natural selection it is exceedingly difficult, as Darwin pointed out, to keep it always firmly in mind. Neglect of natural selection in ecological thinking is, therefore, understandable though regretable. However, its deliberate exclusion in these years following the Darwin centennial would seem to be exceedingly unwise.

Conclusions

The roots of the current controversy which so deeply divides ecology lie much deeper than their peripheral manifestations in the argument over density-dependence and density-independence. Rather, they stem from the division of the field into two major categories—functional ecology and evolutionary ecology. Both of these approahes are valid and useful and it is a mistake to erect general ecological theory exclusively on either.

Acknowledgments

The development and clarification of the ideas presented here has been greatly helped by discussions with students in my advanced ecology class during the past two years, and I gratefully acknowledge their substantial contributions. Also, F. A. Pitelka, W. T. Edmondson and A. J. Kohn read the manuscript and made helpful suggestions.

Literature Cited

Andrewartha, H. G., 1961, Introduction to the study of animal populations. Univ. Chicago Press, Chicago. 281 pp.

Andrewartha, H. G., and L. C. Birch, 1954, The distribution and abundance of animals. Univ. Chicago Press, Chicago. 782 pp.

Birch, L. C., 1955, Selection in *Drosophila pseudoobscura* in relation to crowding. Evolution 9: 389–399.
1960, The genetic factor in population ecology. Am. Naturalist 94: 5–24.
1961, Natural selection between two species of Tephritid fruit fly of the *Genus Dacus*. Evolution 15: 360–374.

Bodmer, W. F., and A. W. F. Edwards, 1960, Natural selection and the sex ratio. Ann. Human Genet. 24: 239–244.

Brown, W. J., Jr., and E. O. Wilson, 1956, Character displacement. Systematic Zool. 5: 49–64.

Cowan, I. McT., W. S. Hoar and J. Hatter, 1950, The effect of forest succession upon the quality and upon the nutritive values of woody plants used as food by moose. Canadian J. Research 28: 249–271.

Dobzhansky, Th., 1957, Mendelian populations as genetic systems. Cold Spring Harbor Symp. Quant. Biol. 22: 385–393.

Elton, C., 1949, Population interspersion: an essay on animal community patterns. J. Ecol. 37: 1–23.

Fisher, R. A., 1958, The genetical theory of natural selection. Dover, New York. 291 pp.

Hairston, N. G., F. H. Smith and L. B. Slobodkin, 1960, Community structure, population control, and competition. Am. Naturalist 94: 421–425.

Harlan, J. R., 1956, Theory and dynamics of grassland agriculture. Van Nostrand, Princeton, N. J. 281 pp.

Hutchinson, G. E., 1953, The concept of pattern in ecology. Proc. Acad. Nat. Sci., Phil., 105: 1–12.
1959, Homage to Santa Rosalia or Why are there so many kinds of animals? Am. Naturalist 93: 145–159

Kohn, A. J., 1959, The ecology of *Conus* in Hawaii. Ecol. Monographs 29: 47–90.

Kolman, W. A., 1960, The mechanism of natural selection for the sex ratio. Am. Naturalist 94: 373–378.

Lack, D., 1954, The natural regulation of animal numbers. Oxford Univ. Press, Oxford. 343 pp.

Lack, D., and H. N. Southern, 1949, Birds on Tenerife. Ibis 91: 607–626.

MacArthur, R. H., 1957, On the relative abundance of bird species. Proc. Natl. Acad. Sci. U.S. 43: 293–295.
1960, On the relative abundance of species. Am. Naturalist 94: 25–36.
1961, Population effects of natural selection. Am. Naturalist 95: 195–199.

MacArthur, R. H., and J. W. MacArthur, 1961, On bird species diversity. Eclogy 42: 594–598.

Mayr, E., 1961, Cause and effect in biology. Science 134: 1501–1506.

Medawar, P. B., 1957, The uniqueness of the individual. Methuen, London. 191 pp.

Orians, G. H., 1960, Social stimulation among blackbird colonies. Condor 62: 330–337.
1961, The ecology of blackbird (*Agelaius*) social organization. Ecol. Monographs 31: 285–312.

Orians, G. H., and F. A. Pitelka, 1960, Range management for the animal ecologist. Ecology 41: 406.

Pitelka, F. A., 1959, Numbers, breeding schedule, and territoriality in Pectoral Sandpipers of Northern Alaska. Condor 61: 233–264.

Pittendrigh, C. S., 1958, Adaptation, natural selection, and behavior. *In:* A. Roe and G. G. Simpson [eds.], Behavior and evolution. Yale Univ. Press, New Haven, Conn. 557 pp.

Simpson, G. G., C. S. Pittendrigh and L. H. Tiffany, 1957, Life. Harcourt, Brace and Company, New York. 845 pp.

Smith, F. E., 1961, Density dependence in Australian thrips. Ecology 42: 403–407.

Taber, R. D., 1956, Deer nutrition and population dynamics in the North Coast Range of California. Trans. Twenty-first North American Wildlife Conf.: 159–172.

Vaurie, C., 1951, Adaptive differences between two sympatric species of Nuthatches (*Sitta*). Proc. X Intern. Ornithol. Congr. 1950: 163–166.

4 / Ecology

Ecology, which emerged as a discipline only in this century, began with investigations into plant geography. Now it can be defined simply as the scientific study of ecosystems. In a short paper F. C. Evans underlines the fundamental importance of the ecosystem concept. A general statement of this concept is provided by E. P. Odum, who, with his brother H. T. Odum, has pioneered the ecosystem approach in America. In this paper Odum outlines the several ecological processes that develop from and relate to the nature of the ecosystem.

One of the classical aspects of ecology relating to the ecosystem is population ecology. An extract from a paper by the well-known American investigator R. E. MacArthur illustrates a modern study in this classical field. A short paper by N. G. Hairston, F. E. Smith, and L. B. Slobodkin, develops further aspects of population ecology.

Space does not permit the inclusion of any work on ecosystem productivity, a subject sometimes referred to as *bioenergetics*. Productivity studies in the past have been effected mostly in aquatic ecosystems, but a number of terrestrial investigations have now been reported.

Ecosystem as the Basic Unit in Ecology

Francis C. Evans

The term *ecosystem* was proposed by Tansley (1935) as a name for the interaction system comprising living things together with their nonliving habitat. Tansley regarded the ecosystem as including "not only the organism-complex, but also the whole complex of physical factors forming what we call the environment." He thus applied the term specifically to that level of biological organization represented by such units as the community and the biome. I here suggest that it is logically appropriate and desirable to extend the application of the concept and the term to include organization levels other than that of the community.

In its fundamental aspects, an ecosystem involves the circulation, transformation, and accumulation of energy and matter through the medium of living things and their activities. Photosynthesis, decomposition, herbivory, predation, parasitism, and other symbiotic activities are among the principal biological processes responsible for the transport and storage of materials and energy, and the interactions of the organisms engaged in these activities provide the pathways of distribution. The food-chain is an

Reprinted by permission of the author and publisher from *Science, 123:* 1127–28, 1956.

example of such a pathway. In the nonliving part of the ecosystem, circulation of energy and matter is completed by such physical processes as evaporation and precipitation, erosion and deposition. The ecologist, then, is primarily concerned with the quantities of matter and energy that pass through a given ecosystem and with the rates at which they do so. Of almost equal importance, however, are the kinds of organisms that are present in any particular ecosystem and the roles that they occupy in its structure and organization. Thus, both quantitative and qualitative aspects need to be considered in the description and comparison of ecosystems.

Ecosystems are further characterized by a multiplicity of regulatory mechanisms, which, in limiting the numbers of organisms present and in influencing their physiology and behavior, control the quantities and rates of movement of both matter and energy. Processes of growth and reproduction, agencies of mortality (physical as well as biological), patterns of immigration and emigration, and habits of adaptive significance are among the more important groups of regulatory mechanisms. In the absence of such mechanisms, no ecosystem could continue to persist and maintain its identity.

The assemblage of plants and animals visualized by Tansley as an integral part of the ecosystem usually consists of numerous species, each represented by a population of individual organisms. However, each population can be regarded as an entity in its own right, interacting with its environment (which may include other organisms as well as physical features of the habitat) to form a system of lower rank that likewise involves the distribution of matter and energy. In turn, each individual animal or plant, together with its particular microenvironment, constitutes a system of still lower rank. Or we may wish to take a world view of life and look upon the biosphere with its total environment as a gigantic ecosystem. Regardless of the level on which life is examined, the ecosystem concept can appropriately be applied. The ecosystem thus stands as a basic unit of ecology, a unit that is as important to this field of natural science as the species is to taxonomy and systematics. In any given case, the particular level on which the ecosystem is being studied can be specified with a qualifying adjective—for example, community ecosystem, population ecosystem, and so forth.

All ranks of ecosystems are open systems, not closed ones. Energy and matter continually escape from them in the course of the processes of life, and they must be replaced if the system is to continue to function. The pathways of loss and replacement of matter and energy frequently connect one ecosystem with another, and therefore it is often difficult to determine the limits of a given ecosystem. This has led some ecologists to reject the exosystem concept as unrealistic and of little use in description or analysis. One is reminded, however, of the fact that it is also difficult, if not impossible, to delimit a species from its ancestral or derivative species or from both; yet this does not destroy the value of the concept. The ecosystem concept may indeed be more useful when it is employed in relation to the community than to the population or individual, for its limits may be more easily determined on that level. Nevertheless, its application to all levels seems fully justified.

The concept of the ecosystem has been described under many names, among them those of *microcosm* (Forbes, 1887), *naturkomplex* (Markus, 1926), *holoceon* (Friederichs, 1930), and *biosystem* (Thlenemann, 1939). Tansley's term seems most successfully to convey its meaning and has in fact been accepted by a large number of present-day ecologists. I hope that it will eventually be adopted universally and that its application will be expanded beyond its original use to include other levels of biological organization. Recognition of the ecosystem as the basic unit in ecology would be helpful in focusing attention upon the truly fundamental aspects of this rapidly developing science.

References

Forbes, S. A. (1887), Bull. Peoria Sci. Assoc.

Friederichs, K. (Parey, Berlin, 1930), Die Grundfragen und Gesetzmassigkeiten der land-und forstwirtschaftlichen Zoologie.

Markus, E. (1926), Sitzber, Naturforsch. Ges. Univ. Tartu **32,** 79.

Tansley, A. G. (1935), Ecology **16,** 296.

Thienemann, K. (1959), Arch. Hydrobiol. **35,** 267.

Relationships Between Structure and Function in the Ecosystem

Eugene P. Odum

As you know, ecology is often defined as: The study of interrelationships between organisms and environment. I feel that this conventional definition is not suitable; it is too vague and too broad. Personally, I prefer to define ecology as: The study of the structure and function of ecosystems. Or we might say in a less technical way: The study of structure and function of nature.

By structure we mean: (1) The composition of the biological community including species, numbers, biomass, life history and distribution in

Reprinted by permission of the author and publisher from *The Japanese Journal of Ecology, 12:* 108–18, 1962.

space of populations; (2) the quantity and distribution of the abiotic (non-living) materials such as nutrients, water, etc.; (3) the range, or gradient, of conditions of existence such as temperature, light, etc. Dividing ecological structure into these three divisions is, of course, arbitrary but I believe convenient for actual study of both aquatic and terrestrial situations.

By function we mean: (1) The rate of biological energy flow through the ecosystem, that is, the rates of production and the rates of respiration of the populations and the community; (2) the rate of material or nutrient cycling, that is, the biogeochemical cycles; (3) biological or ecological regulation including both regulation of organisms by environment (as, for example, in photoperiodism) and regulation of environment by organisms (as, for example, in nitrogen fixation by micro-organisms). Again, dividing ecological function into these three divisions is arbitrary but convenient for study.

Until recently ecologists have been largely concerned with structure, or what we might call the descriptive approach. They were content to describe the conditions of existence and the standing crop of organisms and materials. In recent years equal emphasis is being placed on the functional approach as indicated by the increasing number of studies on productivity and biological regulation. Also the use of experimental methods, both in the field and in the laboratory, has increased. Today, there exists a very serious gap between the descriptive and the functional approach. It is very important that we bring together these two schools of ecology. I should like to present some suggestions for bridging this gap.

The main features of the structure of a terrestrial and an aquatic ecosystem may be illustrated by comparing an open water community, such as might be found at sea or in a large lake, with a land community such as a forest. In our discussion we shall consider these two types as models for the extremes in a gradient of communities which occur in our biosphere. Thus, such ecosystems as estuaries, marshes, shallow lakes, grasslands and agricultural croplands will have a community structure intermediate between the open water and forest types.

Both aquatic and terrestrial community types have several structural features in common. Both must have the same three necessary biological components: (1) Producers or green plants capable of fixing light energy (i.e., autotrophs); (2) animals or macro-consumers which consume particulate organic matter (i.e., phagotrophs); and (3) microorganism decomposers which dissolve organic matter releasing nutrients (i.e., osmotrophs). Both ecosystems must be supplied with the same vital materials such as nitrogen, phosphorus, trace minerals, etc. Both ecosystems are regulated and limited by the same conditions of existence such as light and temperature. Finally, the arrangement of biological units in vertical space is basically the same in the two contrasting types of ecosystems.

Both have two strata, an autotrophic stratum above and a heterotrophic stratum below. The photosynthetic machinery is concentrated in the upper stratum or photic zone where light is available, while the consumer-nutrient regenerating machinery is concentrated largely below the photic zone. It is important to emphasize that while the vertical extent or thickness of communities varies greatly (especially in water), light energy comes into the ecosystem on a horizontal surface basis which is everywhere the same. Thus, different ecosystems should be compared on a square meter basis, not on a cubic or volume basis.

On the other hand, aquatic and terrestrial ecosystems differ in structure in several important ways. Species composition is, of course, completely different; the roles of producers, consumers and decomposers are carried out by taxonomically different organisms which have become adapted through evolution. Trophic structure also differs in that land plants tend to be large in size but few in number while the autotrophs of open water ecosystems (i.e., phytoplankton) are small in size but very numerous. In general, autotrophic biomass is much greater than heterotrophic biomass on land, while the reverse is often true in the sea. Perhaps the most important difference is the following: The matrix, or supporting framework, of the community is largely physical in aquatic ecosystems, but more strongly biological on land. That is to say, the community itself is important as a habitat on land, but not so important in water.

Now, we may ask: How do these similarities and differences in structure affect ecological function?

One important aspect of function is shown in Fig. 1 which compares energy flow in an aquatic and a terrestrial ecosystem. The upper diagram is an energy flow model for a marine community; the lower diagram is a comparable model for a forest. The boxes represent the average standing crop biomass of organisms to be expected; the light gray boxes are the autotrophs, the darker boxes are the heterotrophs. Three trophic levels are shown: (1) Producers, the phytoplankton of the sea and the leaves of the forest trees; (2) primary consumers (herbivores, etc.); and (3) secondary consumers (carnivores). The pipes or flow channels represent the energy flow through the ecosystems beginning with the incoming solar energy and passing through the successive trophic levels. At each transfer a large part of the energy is dissipated in respiration and passes out of the system as heat. The amount of energy remaining after three steps is so small that it can be ignored insofar as the energetics of the community are concerned. However, tertiary consumers ("top carnivores") can be important as regulators; that is, predation may have an important effect on energy flow at the herbivore level.

All numbers in the diagrams are in terms of large or Kilogram Calories and square meters; standing crop is in terms of KCal./M^2; energy flow is in terms of KCal./M^2/day. The diagrams are drawn so that the area of the boxes and the pipes are proportional to the magnitude of the standing crops and energy flows respectively. The quantities shown are a composite of measurements obtained in several different studies; some of the figures for higher trophic levels are hypothetical since complete information is not yet available for any one ecosystem. The marine community is particularly based on the work of Gorden RILEY (Long Island Sound) and H. W. HARVEY (English Channel), and the forest on the work of J. D. OVINGTON (pine forest) and unpublished data on terrestrial communities from our research group at the University of Georgia.

The autotrophic-heterotrophic stratification, which we emphasized as a universal feature of community structure, results in two basic food chains as shown in both diagrams (Fig. 1). The consumption of living plants by herbivores which live in the autotrophic stratum together with their predators may be considered as the *grazing food chain.* This is the classical food chain of ecology, as, for example, the phytoplankton-zooplankton-fish sequence or the grass-rabbit-fox sequence. However, a large proportion of the net production may not be consumed until dead, thus becoming the start of a rather different energy flow which we may conveniently designate as the *detritus food chain.* This energy flow takes place largely in the heterotrophic stratum. As shown in Fig. 1 the detritus energy flow takes place chiefly in the sediments of water systems, and in the litter and soil of land systems.

Ecologists have too often overlooked the fact that the detritus food chain is the more important energy pathway in many ecosystems. As shown in Fig. 1 a larger portion of net production is estimated to be consumed by grazers in the marine bay than in the forest; nine-tenths of the net production of the forest is estimated to be consumed as detritus (dead leaves, wood, etc.). It is not clear whether this difference is a direct or indirect result of the difference in community structure. One tentative generalization might be proposed as follows: communities of small, rapidly growing producers such as phytoplankton or grass can tolerate heavier grazing pressure than communities of large, slow-growing plants such as trees or large seaweeds.

Grazing is one of the most important practical problems facing mankind; yet we know very little about the situation in natural ecosystems. Well-ordered and stable ecosystems seem to have numerous mechanisms which prevent excessive grazing of the living plants. Sometimes, predators appear to provide the chief regulation; sometimes weather or life history characteristics (limited generation time or limited number of generations of herbivores) appear to exercise control. Unfortunately, man with his cattle, sheep and goats often fails to provide such regulation with result that overgrazing and declining productivity is apparent in large areas of the world, especially in grasslands. A study of the division of energy flow between grazing and detritus pathways in stable natural

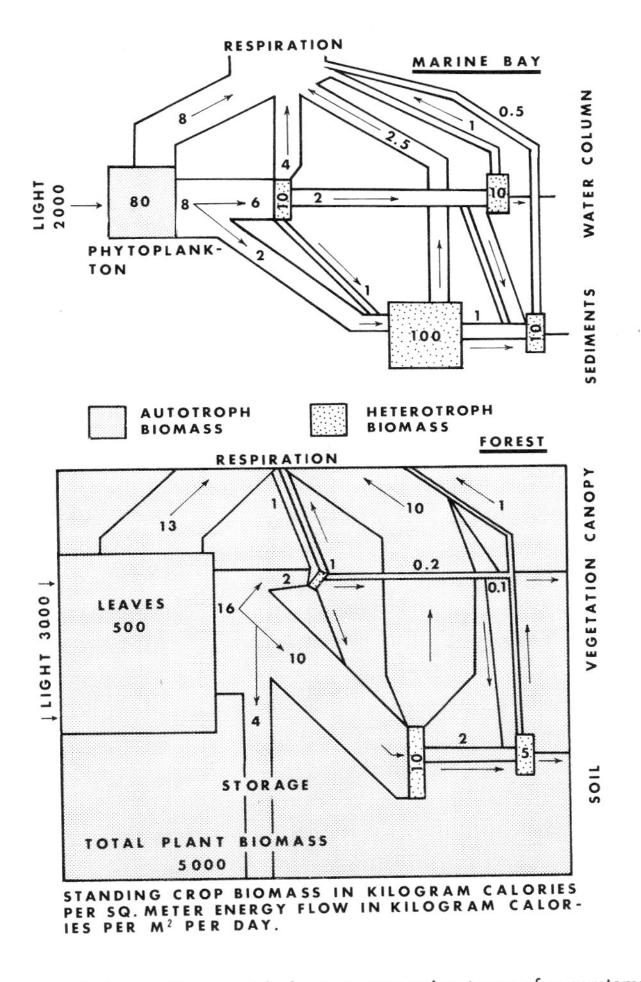

Fig. 1. Energy flow models for two contrasting types of ecosystems, an open water marine ecosystem (upper diagram) and a terrestrial forest (lower diagram).

Standing crop biomass (in terms of KCal./M^2) and trophic structure are shown by means of shaded rectangles. Energy flows in terms of KCal/M^2/day (average annual rate) are shown by means of the unshaded flow channels. The aquatic system is characterized by a small biomass structure (hence the habitat is largely physical) while the forest has a very large biomass structure (hence the habitat is strongly biological). In both types of systems the energy of net primary production passes along two major pathways or food chains: (1) the grazing food chain (upper sequence in the water column or vegetation), and (2) the detritus food chain (lower sequence in sediments or soil).

The marine diagram is based on work of RILEY and HARVEY, the forest diagram on the work of OVINGTON and unpublished data from research at the University of Georgia. In some cases figures are hypothetical since no complete study has yet been made of any ecosystem. Hence, the diagrams should be considered as "working models" which do not represent any one situation.

ecosystems can provide a guide for man's utilization of grasslands, forests, the sea, etc.

The energy flow diagrams, as shown in Fig. 1, reemphasize the difference in biomass as mentioned previously. Autotrophic biomass is very large and envelops or encloses the whole community in the forest; such extensive biological structure buffers and modifies physical factors such as temperature and moisture. In contrast, the aquatic community stands naked or exposed to the direct action of physical factors. In the marine situation the animal biomass often exceed the plant biomass, the sessile animals (oysters, barnacles, etc.) instead of plants often provide some protection or habitat for other organisms.

Despite the large difference in relative size of standing crops in the two extreme types of ecosystems, the actual energy flow may be of the same order of magnitude if light and available nutrients are similar. In Fig. 1 we have shown the available light (absorbed light) and the resulting net production as being somewhat lower in the marine community, but this may not always be true. Thus, 80 KCals of phytoplankton may have a net production almost as large as 5000 KCals of trees (or 500 KCals of green leaves). Therefore, productivity is not proportional to the size of the standing crop except in special cases involving annual plants (as in some agriculture). Unfortunately, many ecologists confuse productivity and standing crop. The relation between structure and function in this case depends on the size and rate of metabolism (and rate of turnover) of the organisms.

To summarize, we see that biological structure influences the pattern of energy flow, particularly the fate of net production and the relative importance of grazers and detritus consumers. However, total energy flow is less affected by structure, and is thus less variable than standing crop. A functional homeostasis has been evolved in nature despite the wide range in species structure and in biomass structure.

So far we have dealt with structure in relation to one aspect of function of the entire ecosystem. Now let us turn to structure and function at the population level and consider a second major aspect of function, namely, the cycling of nutrients. As an example I shall review the work of Dr. Edward J. KUENZLER at the University of Georgia Marine Institute on Sapelo Island. The study concerned a species of mussel of the genus *Modiolus* in the intertidal salt marshes. There are similar species of filter-feeding mollusca in the intertidal zone in all parts of the northern hemisphere.

First, we shall take a look at the salt marsh ecosystem and the distribution of the species in the marsh. The mussels live partly buried in the sediments and attached to the stems and rhyzomes of the marsh grass, *Spartina alterniflora*. Individuals are grouped into colonies (clumped distribution), but the colonies are widely scattered over the marsh.

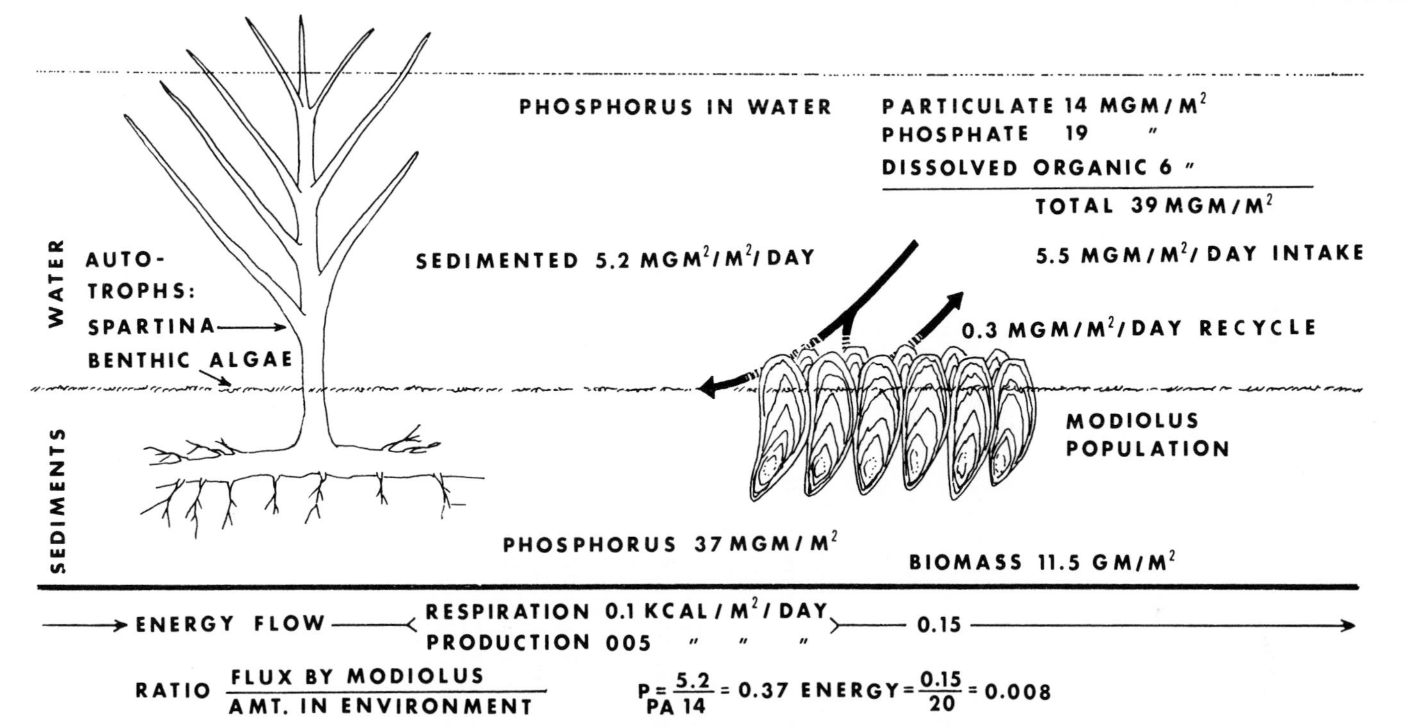

Fig. 2. The effect of a population of mussels (*Modiolus*) on energy flow and the cycling of phosphorus in a salt marsh ecosystem according to the study of Dr. E. J. Kuenzler (1961) at the University of Georgia Marine Institute, Sapelo Island, Georgia, U.S.A.

From the standpoint of the ecosystem as a whole the population has a much greater effect on the transformation of energy. The study illustrates one often overlooked function of animals, that of nutrient regeneration. See text for details of the study.

Numbers average $8/M^2$ for the entire marsh and $32/M^2$ in the most favorable parts of the marsh. Biomass in terms of ash-free dry weight averages 11.5 gms/M^2. When the tide covers the colonies the valves partly open and the animals begin to pump large quantities of water.

Fig. 2 illustrates the role of the mussel population in phosphorus cycling and energy flow according to Dr. KUENZLER's data. Each day the population removes a large part of the phosphorus from the water, especially the particulate fraction. Most of this does not actually pass through the body but is sedimented in the form of pseudofeces which fall on the sediments. Thus, the mussel make large quantities of phosphorus available to microorganisms and to the autotrophs (benthic algae and marsh grass). As shown along the botton of the diagram (Fig. 2) the energy flow was estimated to be about $0.15KCals/M^2/day$.

The most important finding of the study is summarized in the bottom line below the diagram (Fig. 2) which shows the ratio between flux and amount. Note that over one third of the 14 mgms of particulate phosphorus is removed from the water each day by the population, and there by retained in the marsh. In contrast, less than one per cent of the 20 KCals of potential energy (net production estimate) available is actually utilized by the mussel population. In other words, the mussel population has a much more important effect on the community phosphorus cycle than it has on community energy flow. Or one might say that the role of the mussel in conserving nutrients in the ecosystem is more important than its role as energy transformer. In other words, the mussel population would be of comparatively little importance as food for man or animals (since population growth or production is small), but is of great importance in maintaining high primary production of the ecosystem.

To summarize, the mussel study brings out two important points: (1) It is necessary to study both energy flow and biogeochemical cycles to determine the role of a particular species in its ecosystem, (2) animals may be important in the ecosystem not only in terms of food energy, but as agents which make basic nutrient more available to autotrophs.

Finally, I think it is highly significant that the most productive ecosystems of the biosphere are those in which autotrophic and heterotrophic strata lie close together, thus insuring efficient nutrient regeneration and recycling. Estuaries, marshes, coral reefs and rice fields are examples of such productive ecosystems.

Now let us consider the third important aspect of ecological function, that is, community regulation. Ecological succession is one of the most important processes which result from the community modifying the environment. Fig. 3 illustrates a very simple type of ecological succession which can be demonstrated in a laboratory experiment. Yet the basic pattern shown here is the same as occurs in more complex succession of natural communities. The diagram (Fig. 3) was suggested to me by Dr.

Ramon MARGELEF, hence we may call it the MARGELEF model of succession.

At the top of the diagram (Fig. 3) are a series of culture flasks containing plankton communities in different stages of succession. The graph shows changes in two aspects of structure and in one aspect of function. The first flask on the left contains an old and relatively stable community; this flask represents the climax. Diversity of species is high in the climax; species of diatoms, green flagellates, dinoflagellates and rotifers are shown in the diagram to illustrate the variety of plants and animals present. Biochemical diversity is also high as indicated by the ratio of yellow plant pigments (optical density at 430mu) to chlorophyll-a (optical density at 665mu). On the other hand the ratio of production to biomass (P/B in Fig. 3) is low in the old or climax culture, and gross production tends to equal community respiration. If we add fresh culture medium to the old culture, as shown in Fig. 3, ecological succession is set in motion. An early stage in succession is shown in the second flask. Species diversity is low, with one or two species of phytoplankton dominant. Chlorophylls predominate so that the yellow/green ratio (O.D. 430/O.D. 665) is low, indicating low biochemical diversity. On the other hand, production now exceeds respiration so that the ratio of production to biomass becomes higher. In other words, autotrophy greatly exceed heterotrophy in the pioneer or early succession stage. The two flasks on the right side of the diagram (Fig. 3) show the gradual return to the climax or steady state where autotrophy tends to balance heterotrophy.

The changes which we have just described are apparently typical of all succession regardless of environment or type of ecosystem. Although much more study is needed, it appears that differences in community structure mainly affect the time required, that is, whether the horizontal scale (X-axis in Fig. 3) is measured in weeks, months or years. Thus, in open water ecosystems, as in cultures, the community is able to modify the physical environment to only a small extent. Consequently, succession in such ecosystems is brief, lasting perhaps for only a few weeks. In a typical marine pond or shallow marine bay a brief succession from diatoms to dinoflagellates occurs each season, or perhaps several times each season. Aquatic ecosystems characterized by strong currents or other physical forces may exhibit no ecological succession at all, since the community is not able to modify the physical environment. Changes observed in such ecosystems are the direct result of physical forces, and are not the result of biological processes; consequently, such changes are not to be classed as ecological succession.

In a forest ecosystem, on the other hand, a large biomass accumulates with time, which means that the community continues to change in species composition and continues to regulate and buffer the physical

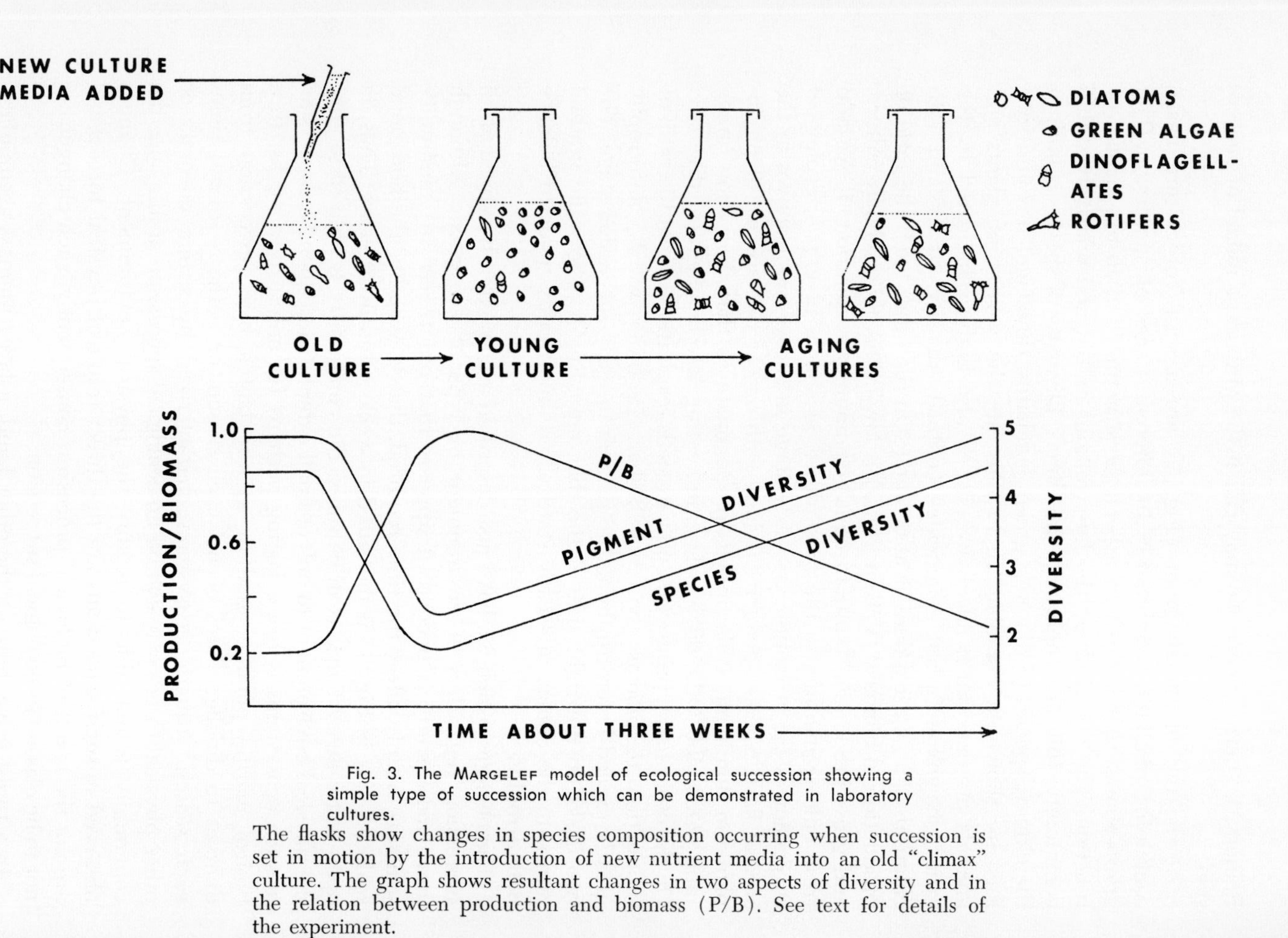

Fig. 3. The MARGELEF model of ecological succession showing a simple type of succession which can be demonstrated in laboratory cultures.

The flasks show changes in species composition occurring when succession is set in motion by the introduction of new nutrient media into an old "climax" culture. The graph shows resultant changes in two aspects of diversity and in the relation between production and biomass (P/B). See text for details of the experiment.

environment to a greater and greater degree. Let us refer again to Fig. 1 which compares a forest with an aquatic ecosystem. The very large biological structure of the forest enables the community to buffer the physical environment and to change the substrate and the micro-climate to a greater extent than is possible in the marine community.

Recent studies on primary succession on such sites as sand dunes or recent volcanic lava flows indicate that at least 1000 years may be required for development of the climax. Secondary succession on cut-over forest land or abandoned agricultural land is more rapid, but at least 200 years may be required for development of the stable climax community. When the climate is severe as, for example, in deserts, grasslands or tundras the duration of ecological succession is short since the community can not modify the harsh physical environment to a very large extent.

To summarize, I am suggesting that the basic pattern of functional change in ecological succession is the same in all ecosystems, but that the species composition, rate of change and duration of succession is determined by the physical environment and the resultant community structure.

The principles of ecological succession are of the greatest importance to mankind. Man must have early successional stages as a source of food since he must have a large net primary production to harvest; in the climax community production is mostly consumed by respiration (plant and animal) so that net community production in an annual cycle may be zero. On the other hand, the stability of the climax and its ability to buffer and control physical forces (such as water and temperature) are desirable characteristics from the viewpoint of human population. The only way man can have both a productive and a stable environment is to insure that a good mixture of early and mature successional stages (i.e. "young nature" and "old nature") are maintained with interchanges of energy and materials. Excess food produced in young communities helps feed older stages which in return supply regenerated nutrients and help buffer the extremes of weather (storms, floods, etc.).

Population Ecology of Some Warblers of Northeastern Coniferous Forests

Robert H. MacArthur

Discussion and Conclusions

In this study competition has been viewed in the light of the statement that species can coexist "only if each inhibits its own population more than the others." This is probably equivalent to saying that species divide

Reprinted by permission of the author and publisher from *Ecology, 39:* 599–619, 1958.

up the resources of a community in such a way that each species is limited by a different factor. If this is taken as a statement of the Volterra-Gause principle, there can be no exceptions to it. Ecological investigations of closely-related species then are looked upon as enumerations of the divers ways in which the resources of a community can be partitioned.

For the five species of warbler considered here, there are three quite distinct categories of "different factors" which could regulate populations. "Different factors" can mean different resources, the same resources at different places, or the same resources at different times. All three of these seem important for the warblers, especially if different places and times mean very different-different habitats and different years.

First, the observations show that there is every reason to believe that the birds behave in such a way as to be exposed to different kinds of food. They feed in different positions, indulge in hawking and hovering to different extents, move in different directions through the trees, vary from active to sluggish, and probably have the greatest need for food at different times corresponding to the different nesting dates. All of these differences are statistical, however; any two species show some overlapping in all of these activities. The species of food organisms which were widespread in the forest and had high dispersal rates would be preyed upon by all the warblers. Thus, competition for food is possible. The actual food eaten does indicate that the species have certain foods in common. The slight difference in habitat preferance resulting from the species' different feeding zones is probably more important. This could permit each species to have its own center of dispersal to regions occupied by all species. Coexistence in one habitat, then, may be the result of each species being limited by the availability of a resource in different habitats. Even although the insects fed upon may be basically of the same type in the different habitats, it is improbable that the same individual insects should fly back and forth between distant woods; consequently, there would be no chance for competition. The habitat differences and, equivalently, the feeding zone differences, between blackburnian, black-throated green, and bay-breasted are sufficiently large that this explanation of coexistence is quite reasonable.

The myrtle warbler is present in many habitats in the summer but is never abundant. It has a very large summer and winter range, feeds from the tree tops to the forest floor, and by rapid peering or by hawking. It makes frequent long flights and defends a large territory. Probably it can be considered a marginal species which, by being less specialized and thus more flexible in its requirements, manages to maintain a constant, low population.

The Cape May warbler is in a different category, at least in the region near the southern limit of its range. For here it apparently depends upon the occasional outbreaks of superabundant food (usually spruce budworms) for its continued existence. The bay-breasted warbler, to a lesser degree, does the same thing. During budworm outbreaks, probably because of their extra large clutches, they are able to increase more rapidly than the other species, obtaining a temporary advantage. During the years between outbreaks they suffer reductions in numbers and may even be eliminated locally. Lack's hypothesis, that the clutch is adjusted so as to produce the maximum number of surviving offspring, provides a suitable explanation of the decrease during normal years of these large-clutched species. It may be asked why, if Lack's hypothesis is correct, natural selection favored large clutches in Cape May and bay-breasted. Cheshire's censuses suggest a tentative answer. During his years of censusing, increase in the bay-breasted warbler population reached a figure of over 300% per year. This probably far exceeds the maximum possible increase due to survival of nestlings raised in that place; probably immigration is the explanation. But if the species with large clutches search for areas in which food is superabundant and immigrate into these regions, then, for the species as a whole, the large clutch may be adapted to the maximum survival of offspring. Cape May and bay-breasted warblers may therefore be considered to be good examples of fugitive species.

Thus, of the five species, Cape May warblers and to a lesser degree bay-breasted warblers are dependent upon periods of superabundant food, while the remaining species maintain populations roughly proportional to the volume of foliage of the type in which they normally feed. There are differences of feeding position, behavior, and nesting date which reduce competition. These, combined with slight differences in habitat preference and perhaps a tendency for territoriality to have a stronger regulating effect upon the same species than upon others, permit the coexistence of the species.

Community Structure, Population Control, and Competition

Nelston G. Hairston
Frederick E. Smith
Lawrence B. Slobodkin

The methods whereby natural populations are limited in size have been debated with vigor during three decades, particularly during the last few years (see papers by Nicholson, Birch, Andrewartha, Milne,

Reprinted by permission of the authors and publisher from *The American Naturalist*, *94:* 421–25, 1960.

Reynoldson, and Hutchinson, and ensuing discussions in the Cold Spring Harbor Symposium, 1957). Few ecologists will deny the importance of the subject, since the method of regulation of populations must be known before we can understand nature and predict its behavior. Although discussion of the subject has usually been confined to single species populations, it is equally important in situations where two or more species are involved.

The purpose of this note is to demonstrate a pattern of population control in many communities which derives easily from a series of general, widely accepted observations. The logic used is not easily refuted. Furthermore, the pattern reconciles conflicting interpretations by showing that populations in different trophic levels are expected to differ in their methods of control.

Our first observation is that the accumulation of fossil fuels occurs at a rate that is negligible when compared with the rate of energy fixation through photosynthesis in the biosphere. Apparent exceptions to this observation, such as bogs and ponds, are successional stages, in which the failure of decomposition hastens the termination of the stage. The rate of accumulation when compared with that of photosynthesis has also been shown to be negligible over geologic time (Hutchinson, 1948).

If virtually all of the energy fixed in photosynthesis does indeed flow through the biosphere, it must follow that all organisms taken together are limited by the amount of energy fixed. In particular, the decomposers as a group must be food-limited, since by definition they comprise the trophic level which degrades organic debris. There is no a priori reason why predators, behavior, physiological changes induced by high densities, etc., could not limit decomposer populations. In fact, some decomposer populations may be limited in such ways. If so, however, others must consume the "left-over" food, so that the group as a whole remains food limited; otherwise fossil fuel would accumulate rapidly.

Any population which is not resource-limited must, of course, be limited to a level *below* that set by its resources.

Our next three observations are interrelated. They apply primarily to terrestrial communities. The first of these is that cases of obvious depletion of green plants by herbivores are exceptions to the general picture, in which the plants are abundant and largely intact. Moreover, cases of obvious mass destruction by meteorological catastrophes are exceptional in most areas. Taken together, these two observations mean that producers are neither herbivore-limited nor catastrophe-limited, and must therefore be limited by their own exhaustion of a resource. In many areas, the limiting resource is obviously light, but in arid regions water may be the critical factor, and there are spectacular cases of limitation through the exhaustion of a critical mineral. The final observation in this group is that there are temporary exceptions to the general lack of depletion of green plants by herbivores. This occurs when herbivores are protected either by man or natural events, and it indicates that the herbivores are able to deplete the vegetation whenever they become numerous enough, as in the cases of the Kaibab deer herd, rodent plagues, and many insect outbreaks. It therefore follows that the usual condition is for populations of herbivores *not* to be limited by their food supply.

The vagaries of weather have been suggested as an adequate method of control for herbivore populations. The best factual clues related to this argument are to be found in the analysis of the exceptional cases where terrestrial herbivores have become numerous enough to deplete the vegetation. This often occurs with introduced rather than native species. It is most difficult to suppose that a species had been unable to adapt so as to escape control by the weather to which it was exposed, and at the same time by sheer chance to be able to escape this control from weather to which it had not been previously exposed. This assumption is especially difficult when mutual invasions by different herbivores between two countries may in both cases result in pests. Even more difficult to accept, however, is the implication regarding the native herbivores. The assumption that the hundreds or thousands of species native to a forest have failed to escape from control by the weather despite long exposure and much selection, when an invader is able to defoliate without this past history, implies that "pre-adaptation" is more likely than ordinary adaptation. This we cannot accept.

The remaining general method of herbivore control is predation (in its broadest sense, including parasitism, etc.). It is important to note that this hypothesis is not denied by the presence of introduced pests, since it is necessary only to suppose that either their natural predators have been left behind, or that while the herbivore is able to exist in the new climate, its enemies are not. There are, furthermore, numerous examples of the direct effect of predator removal. The history of the Kaibab deer is the best known example, although deer across the northern portions of the country are in repeated danger of winter starvation as a result of protection and predator removal. Several rodent plagues have been attributed to the local destruction of predators. More recently, the extensive spraying of forests to kill caterpillars has resulted in outbreaks of scale insects. The latter are protected from the spray, while their beetle predators and other insect enemies are not.

Thus, although rigorous proof that herbivores are generally controlled by predation is lacking, supporting evidence is available, and the alternate hypothesis of control by weather leads to false or untenable implications.

The foregoing conclusion has an important implication in the mechanism of control of the predator populations. The predators and parasites, in controlling the populations of herbivores, must thereby limit their own resources, and as a group they must be food-limited. Although the populations of some carnivores are obviously limited by territoriality, this kind of internal check cannot operate for all carnivores taken together. If it did, the herbivores would normally expand to the point of depletion of the vegetation, as they do in the absence of their normal predators and parasites.

There thus exists either direct proof or a great preponderance of factual evidence that in terrestrial communities decomposer, producers, and predators, as whole trophic levels, are resource-limited in the classical density-dependent fashion. Each of these three can and does expand toward the limit of the appropriate resource. We may now examine the reasons why this is a frequent situation in nature.

Whatever the resource for which a set of terrestrial plant species compete, the competition ultimately expresses itself as competition for space. A community in which this space is frequently emptied through depletion by herbivores would run the continual risk of replacement by another assemblage of species in which the herbivores are held down in numbers by predation below the level at which they damage the vegetation. That space once held by a group of terrestrial plant species is not readily given up is shown by the cases where relict stands exist under climates no longer suitable for their return following deliberate or accidental destruction. Hence, the community in which herbivores are held down in numbers, and in which the producers are resource-limited will be the most persistent. The development of this pattern is less likely where high producer mortalities are inevitable. In lakes, for example, algal populations are prone to crash whether grazed or not. In the same environment, grazing depletion is much more common than in communities where the major producers are rooted plants.

A second general conclusion follows from the resource limitation of the species of three trophic levels. This conclusion is that if more than one species exists in one of these levels, they may avoid competition only if each species is limited by factors completely unutilized by any of the other species. It is a fact, of course, that many species occupy each level in most communities. It is also a fact that they are not sufficiently segregated in their needs to escape competition. Although isolated cases of non-overlap have been described, this has never been observed for an entire assemblage. Therefore, interspecific competition for resources exists among producers, among carnivores, and among decomposers.

It is satisfying to note the number of observations that fall into line with the foregoing deductions. Interspecific competition is a powerful selective force, and we should expect to find evidence of its operation. Moreover, the evidence should be most conclusive in trophic levels where it is necessarily present. Among decomposers we find the most obvious specific mechanisms for reducing populations of competitors. The abundance of antibiotic substances attests to the frequency with which these mechanisms have been developed in the trophic level in which interspecific competition is inevitable. The producer species are the next most likely to reveal evidence of competition, and here we find such phenomena as crowding, shading, and vegetational zonation.

Among the carnivores, however, obvious adaptations for interspecific competition are less common. Active competition in the form of mutual habitat-exclusion has been noted in the cases of flatworms (Beauchamp and Ullyott, 1932) and salamanders (Hairston, 1951). The commonest situation takes the form of niche diversification as the result of interspecific competition. This has been noted in birds (Lack, 1945; MacArthur, 1958), salamanders (Hairston, 1949), and other groups of carnivores. Quite likely, host specificity in parasites and parasitoid insects is at least partly due to the influence of interspecific competition.

Of equal significance is the frequent occurrence among herbivores of apparent exceptions to the influence of density-dependent factors. The grasshoppers described by Birch (1957), and the thrips described by Davidson and Andrewartha (1948) are well known examples. Moreover, it is among herbivores that we find cited examples of coexistence without evidence of competition for resources, such as the leafhoppers reported by Ross (1957), and the psocids described by Broadhead (1958). It should be pointed out that in these latter cases coexistence applies primarily to an identity of food and place, and other aspects of the niches of these organisms are not known to be identical.

Literature Cited

Andrewartha, H. G., 1957, The use of conceptual models in population ecology. Cold Spring Harbor Symp. Quant. Biol. 22: 219–232.

Beauchamp, R. S. A., and P. Ullyott, 1932, Competitive relationships between certain species of fresh-water triclads. J. Ecology 20: 200–208.

Birch, L. C., 1957, The role of weather in determining the distribution and abundance of animals. Cold Spring Harbor Symp. Quant. Biol. 22: 217–263.

Broadhead, E., 1958, The psocid fauna of larch trees in northern England. J. Anim. Ecol. 27: 217–263.

Davidson, J., and H. G. Andrewartha, 1948, The influence of rainfall, evaporation and atmospheric temperature on fluctuations in the size of a natural population of *Thrips imaginis* (Thysanoptera). J. Anim. Ecol. 17: 200–222.

Hairston, N. G., 1949, The local distribution and ecology of the Plethodontid salamanders of the southern Appalachians. Ecol. Monog. 19: 47–73.
1951, Interspecies competition and its probable influence upon the vertical distribution of Appalachian salamanders of the genus Plethodon. Ecology 32: 266–274.

Hutchinson, G. E., 1948, Circular causal systems in ecology. Ann. N. Y. Acad. Sci. 50: 221–246.
1957, Concluding remarks. Cold Spring Harbor Symp. Quant. Biol. 22: 415–427.

Lack, D., 1945, The ecology of closely related species with special reference to cormorant (*Phalacrocorax carbo*) and shag (*P. aristotelis*). J. Anim. Ecol. 14: 12–16.

MacArthur, R. H., 1958, Population ecology of some warblers of northeastern coniferous forests. Ecology 39: 599–619.

Milne, A., 1957, Theories of natural control of insect populations. Cold Spring Harbor Symp. Quant. Biol. 22: 253–271.

Nicholson, A. J., 1957, The self-adjustment of populations to change. Cold Spring Harbor Symp. Quant. Biol. 22: 153–172.

Reynoldson, T. B., 1957, Population fluctuations in *Urceolaria mitra* (Peritricha) and *Enchytraeus albidus* (Oligochaeta) and their bearing on regulation. Cold Spring Harbor Symp. Biol. 22: 313–327.

Ross, H. H., 1957, Principles of natural coexistence indicated by leafhopper populations. Evolution 11: 113–129.

Glossary

Accipitridae bird family of hawks, vultures, and harriers.

alloploid polyploid in which there are two sets of chromosomes of differing form and origin.

allopatric occurring in different geographic areas.

amphiploid having at least one set of chromosomes derived from each parent, but behaving as a diploid.

anagenesis evolution through preadapted characters in a new environment.

angiosperm a plant producing seeds borne within an ovary.

apomictic possessing apomixis.

apomixis reproduction by means of sexual organs without the occurrence of nuclear fusion.

autoploid polyploid in which all the sets of chromosomes are identical in form and origin.

autotrophic producing its own food.

biomass total amount of living matter in a trophic level or ecosystem.

biosphere the complex of living organisms and physical factors affecting them on the earth.

Carnivora order of mammals adapted to eat flesh.

cestode animal belonging to the tape worm group.

chromatography the separation of components in a chemical mixture, utilizing a solvent and a solid absorption agent, commonly paper.

cladogenesis branching of the phylogenetic line.

clone a population that is propagated asexually.

Corvidae bird family of jays, magpies, and crows.

cytology study of the structure, behavior, and reproduction of living cells.

Cretaceous the last period of the Mesozoic era.

deme a neutral suffix denoting any group of individuals of a particular population—e.g., *topodeme* (a group occurring in a specified geographical area) and *ecodeme* (a group occurring in a specific habitat).

diploid having two sets of chromosomes.

ecotype population within a species which has been selected genetically in response to particular ecological conditions.

electrophoresis qualitative chemical separation by the application of an electrical field, utilizing the differing migration rates of the electrolytes.

ethology the study of animal population behavior.

Fringillidae bird family of finches, sparrows, and buntings.

gene the physical unit of the chromosome, determining one or more characters.

genotype the gene complement of a given organism.

heterothermic body temperature fluctuating with that of the environment, not held constant.

heterotrophic requiring food from an external source.

homothermic maintaining a constant body temperature.

Mesozoic the Age of Reptiles, the third of the five eras on the geological scale, succeeding the Palaeozoic era and being replaced by the Cenozoic era.

mutation a genetic variation resulting from a chemical change in a gene, or a physical change in a chromosome.

niche the total environmental factors to which a particular population is exposed.

Ostracoda group of small bivalve crustaceans.

Palaeozoic the "ancient life" era, the second of the five eras on the geological scale, succeeding the Precambrian era and replaced by the Mesozoic era.

passeres suborder of songbirds.

phenotype actual form of an organism, resulting from the interaction between the genotype and the environment.

Pleistocene the period of the last Ice Ages.

polymorphic having a wide variation in form.

polyploid organism, tissue, or cell with more than two complete sets of chromosomes.

phylogenetic pertaining to phylogeny.

phylogenesis modification of the phylogenetic line during evolutionary time.

phylogeny deduced ancestral history.

radiation the evolution of a range of forms varying in many directions.

sibling offspring of identical parental origin.

stasigenesis evolution by natural selection among different forms.

segregation the sorting out of hereditary factors by a random process during reduction division of the nucleus.

taxon (pl., taxa) a discrete population unit of any size, definable on a taxonomic basis.

tetraploid having four sets of chromosomes.

Tertiary interval of geologic time between the close of the Mesozoic era and the Pleistocene Ice Ages.

triploid having three sets of chromosomes.

trophic level group of organisms in an ecosystem with the same type of metabolism.

typogenesis the evolution of new taxa.